EXPECTING THE UNEXPECTED

One Man's Journey Through a Most Eventful Pregnancy

FERREL E. CALPIN

Published by CarpeDiem Publishing

ISBN-10: 1526201623
ISBN-13: 978-1-5262-0162-1

In loving memory of Renée Mary Sarah Whitlock

1921 - 2015

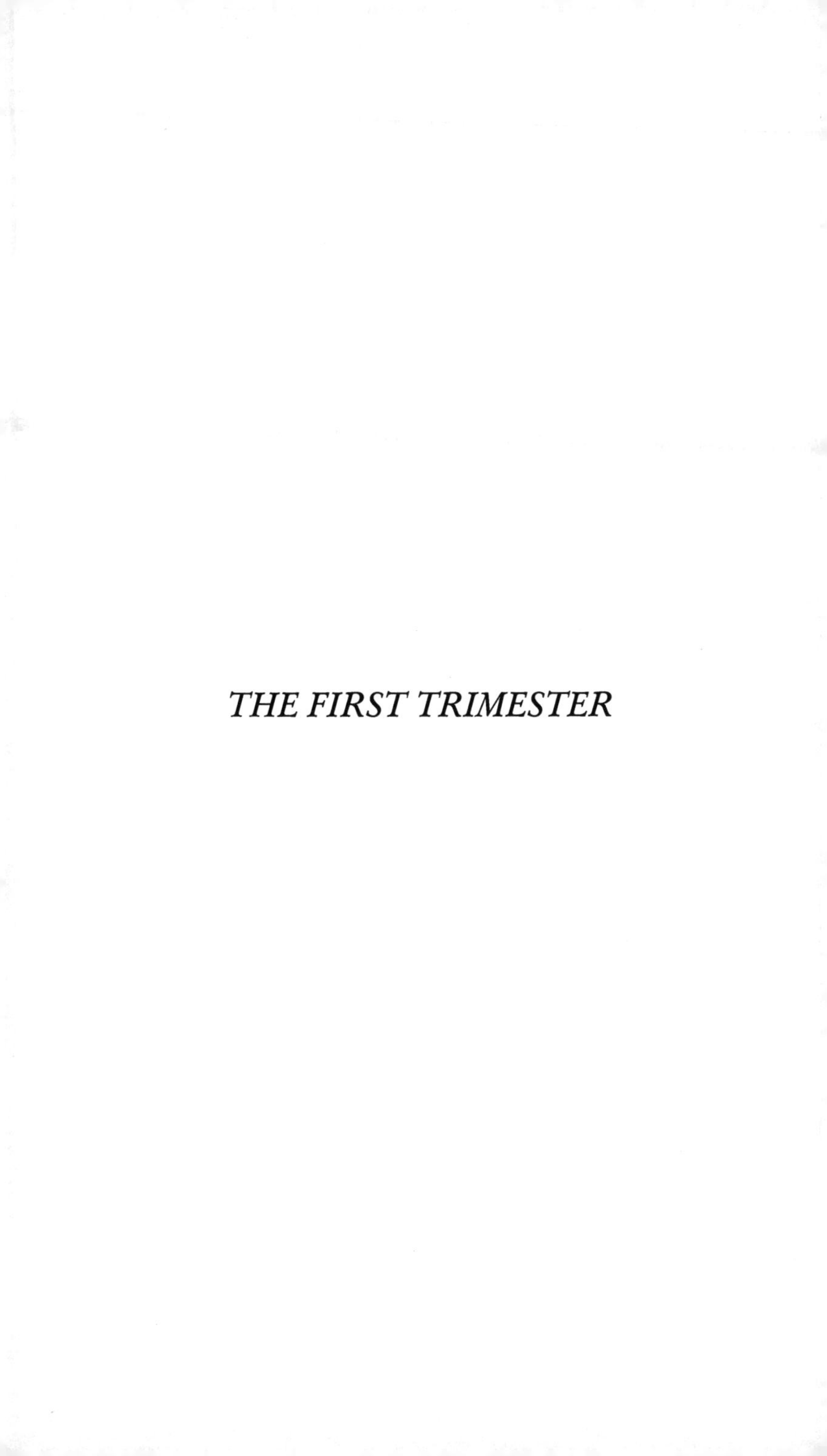

THE FIRST TRIMESTER

1

'I think I'm pregnant!'

It's 4.45am on Sunday morning and my girlfriend Sally is standing by my side of our bed in her winter pyjamas waving what looks like a novelty pen under my nose and grinning from ear-to-ear.

'What?'

She hands the novelty pen to me, her eyes blazing with excitement: 'If there are two lines then it means I'm pregnant.' I focus my own still tired eyes, scrutinise the readout on the sleek little home testing kit and see one bold line and one very faint line.

'Are you sure this is accurate?'

She tells me, in between bouncing uncontrollably from one foot to the other, that her sister's home test looked exactly the same eight-and-a-half months ago and that she will brave the late-November chill and get a digital tester from the supermarket up the road as soon as it opens, just to make sure.

I start to smile: 'So you really could be pregnant?'

She beams even more broadly, gives me a massive hug and proudly confirms what she's been trying to tell me for the last two minutes:

'Yes; YES!!'

My initial reaction is one of genuine joy, as we have been trying for a baby for nearly two years. My second reaction is one of achievement as multiple tests had indicated my sperm count to be less than half what it should be.

Indeed, I felt very joyous and extremely proud. And nowhere near as tired as I did five minutes ago!

'So we'll know for sure when you go to Tesco?'

Yep!'

It's now nearly 5am. Tescos doesn't open for another four hours so Sally retreats from the early morning coldness and climbs back into bed. We snuggle up and endeavour to take in the enormity of it all.

'Doesn't feel real, does it?' she finally says.

I agree, and after what seems like an eternity, we eventually fall back to sleep.

Later

I sleep fitfully as my sub-conscious is awash with all manner of predominantly selfish worries and concerns.
To my surprise, my initial feelings of joy and pride are made to give way pretty quickly for something that resembles anxiety; the kind you get before you're about to take a driving test or make some kind of a speech in public.

Not quite fear – but not far off.

Doubts begin to enter my head: 'Is this what I really, truly want? Am I really ready to take on such a huge responsibility? Does this mean that my life as a 'young man' is effectively over? Suffice to say, the second digital novelty pen Sally bought as soon as Tesco opened confirmed the news we had been waiting so long for.

We really are going to have a baby.

This time we treat ourselves to an extended hug and get back in bed to share the realisation properly. I tell Sally about the anxiety I am now feeling and she agrees that the whole thing is 'very scary'.

With that, my own selfish concerns take a back seat. Sally is one of the kindest and most caring people you could ever hope to meet, and she has waited a long time to be in this position. Working as a nursery nurse and nanny for much of her adult life, and now as a primary school teacher, she has spent many years looking after other peoples' children. She even cared for her elder sister's son and daughter full-time when they were both very young.

To know that she will now, all being well, have the chance to care for a baby all of her own makes me feel incredibly happy for her.

But then - not much later it has to be said – the warm feelings subsided and the doubts returned.

2

So it's been a week since I discovered Sal is pregnant (nearly five weeks 'gone' now).

And, whilst it is fair to say my head was a little bit up my backside for the first 24 hours, I have been genuinely surprised by the way I have accepted the fact I am going to become a father.

The reason I feel surprised is that, for many years, I had conditioned myself to have one response - and only one response - to any scenario which involved me siring an offspring: I would pack up my belongings in less than ten minutes, go straight to Heathrow and catch the first available flight to South America I could find.

It was a gutless, impetuous and totally selfish plan - indeed it was the perfect solution for the man I was back in my twenties. During the past week however, I have had no urge at all to see how reasonable one-way airfares to Brazil are at this time of the year, nor have I been up to the loft to see if my trusty old travelling backpack is still fit for purpose.

This suggests one of two things: I am either dead inside, or I am a different man to the Samba-curious dromomaniac I once was.

Now I'm pretty sure I'm not dead inside (the immediate rage I feel whenever I see a Katie Hopkins' story pop up somewhere assures me of this); therefore I can only conclude I am now at a stage of life when having a child actually seems like a pretty good idea.

Sitting here, pondering this, I can now appreciate that getting to this stage of life has been a long and gradual process. Of course, the thing about long, gradual processes - like going bald or getting fat - is that they are difficult to observe in real time. For sure, the only way to really notice how much balder/fatter/more mature you've become is to have a 'before & after' moment, where the evidence of your new self is clear and irrefutable.

Fifteen years ago, I had only one outlook on life – to live it to the full. And, the only way to do that I concluded was by partying hard and backpacking around the world. To this end, I worked seasonally on British holiday parks and European beach resorts during the spring, summer and autumn, and then went away travelling with nothing but a passport and a backpack for a month or two during the winter.

It has to be said - it was a pretty good life.

And, even when I called time on being a seasonal worker and opted to settle down with Sally, I still managed to squeeze in extended boozing sessions with old pals and enjoy bi-annual backpacking jaunts away to ensure I didn't become a fully paid-up member of the Rat Race.

However, like a full head of hair or a perfectly proportioned waistline, my appetite for this way of living has waned over the last five years or so. I know this because there have been times in recent years when nights out on the lash have not just been disappointing; they have been a veritable test in endurance. Instead of being the very people I made a beeline for, drunken individuals, slurring their words and spilling alcopops everywhere became the people I wanted to avoid.

Me! The man who had almost single-handedly put the beer into 'beer monster' throughout large swathes of the UK, France, Greece and Turkey between 1994 and 2004!

Even my backpacking trips away became different. Instead of finding hostels full of engaging characters with adventurous tales, I seemed only to encounter gap year students who seemed to do little other than brag of how many countries in South-East Asia they had 'done'. The simple fact is, the world I know and the lifestyle – and identity - I spent so long cultivating for myself has changed significantly since I reached my early to mid-thirties. I'm not sure why this is exactly; I'm assuming it's just emotional maturity (finally) kicking in. Whatever the reason might be though, it has happened and there is nothing I can do about it. To fight this phenomenon or even pretend it is not an issue is quite futile. I think I tried this approach on a sub-conscious level a few years back, blaming everything from my mortgage and 'needy' mother to my choice of career and long-term relationship with Sal for the fact I wasn't enjoying life in the same way as I did when I was 21. Needless to say, I wasn't very good company around that time; seemed to feel quite angry a lot of the time as I remember.

But now I am here, about to turn 38 in two days time, a different man and quite happy with it. I no longer feel that a rock n roll-type lifestyle of Oliver Reed-type shenanigans and spontaneous travelling is the only way to be happy. I have been there and done that.

Perhaps the way I feel now can best be articulated by one of the 20th century's most underrated independent thinkers, boxing legend Muhammad Ali. He said: "The man who views the world at 50 the same as he did at 20 has wasted 30 years of his life."

Now that I can see how true this is, I feel that I am not just ready for my life to go in a completely different direction, I genuinely welcome it.

3

Well, it is fair to say that the last week has been something of a roller-coaster.

Funnily enough, the week started brightly enough as Monday was my 38th birthday. My working day came and went nice and swiftly; my Mum and Dad merrily sang *Happy Birthday* to me down the phone, and my celebratory Chinese takeaway and present opening was all ready to start as soon as Sally got back from school.

But things soon took a turn for the worse when she did eventually come through the door in the mid-to-late afternoon. The look on her face immediately told me something definitely wasn't right.

She had been complaining of pains in her side for the last couple of days and had told me that she'd been feeling under the weather in general. I didn't interpret this as being anything to worry about though as Sal – bless her - is someone who gets poorly quite a lot. However, once she told me about the things she had been looking at on the Internet, I became very worried, very quickly. And that is because side pains and general nausea are tell-tale signs of an ectopic pregnancy.

Ectopic means 'in the wrong place'. A pregnancy becomes ectopic when a fertilised egg implants itself outside of the womb, normally in one of the fallopian tubes. This means that the egg will not develop into a baby. Although Sal had an appointment booked to see her GP on Friday, we both decided that the circumstances were serious enough to warrant a more rapid reaction. Therefore, Sal went straight to our local GP surgery to take advantage of the 'Sit & Wait' appointments which enable patients with urgent-ish needs to see a doctor that day. The GP who (eventually) saw Sal gave her a physical examination and told her that, whilst she believed an ectopic pregnancy was unlikely, an appointment with a gynaecological consultant was the best way to proceed.

Within half an hour, we were parked up at our impressive, newly-built local hospital and queuing up at the Accident and Emergency reception desk with a note to see the on-call gynaecological consultant (what with the Early Pregnancy Unit being closed after 5pm).

After waiting for about an hour in the Ikea-inspired holding pen with our local area's finest selection of walking wounded, we were finally called through the secure doors to the inner sanctum by the on-call gynaecological consultant. He was a very friendly middle-aged man who had a laid-back aura which Sal and I found very reassuring.

We were led to a small examination cubicle where Sal was directed to lie down on a bed which the porters had just that moment finished replacing the covers on. Once the curtain had been drawn, the consultant pressed lightly around her abdomen and asked questions about her periods, her recent pains, her general health and something called 'spotting' (I didn't even know she was into bird-watching).

Eventually, he stood up straight, looked over at me sitting in the corner and then sat himself down on the end of the bed.

'Well, I don't think it's an ectopic pregnancy', he said.

I looked over at Sal and, for the first time that day, saw the muscles in her face relax. The consultant went on to explain how he had come to this conclusion and advised us to book an appointment with the hospital's Early Pregnancy Unit, as they would be able to carry out a scan which would provide us with the peace of mind we were looking for.

As he disappeared from the cubicle to consult with other consultants about consulting matters, I gave Sal a hug and stroked her hair. As I did so, she apologised to me for spoiling my birthday. I told her to stop being so silly and reminded her how things could have been a whole lot worse.

After a somewhat lengthy wait (during which time I pocketed every baby first aid advice leaflet I could find), the consultant returned and told us we were free to go and that we should only consider going back if Sally started bleeding or 'spotting' a lot.

After a few more completely unnecessary apologies about spoiling my birthday, Sally was quiet as we drove home. I didn't try to engage her in conversation as it just felt right to have a bit of quiet for a while. When we eventually got back home, I went straight to the kitchen and put the kettle on for a cup of tea (is there any other way of dealing with adversity?). When I came back into the living room, I saw that Sal had arranged my cards and presents into an attractive looking pile for me to open. I gave a half-hearted smile and said that they could wait.

The truth is, I didn't feel like doing anything jovial at that moment. I had woken up that day thinking I was going to be a father; spent most of the afternoon and evening considering the possibility that I might well not, and then bam! – Everything's back on track; I'm going to be a dad again (maybe; hopefully).

At that moment I just felt drained and as such I would have been more than happy to leave the celebrations until tomorrow.

But then I looked again at my presents and at Sal. She was surely feeling a hundred times worse than I was and yet she still had the endeavour in her to arrange my gifts into a handsome little pile. She had kept these concerns to herself for a good few days and had only decided to burden me with them when she thought there may actually be a serious problem.

And they say women are the weaker sex.

So, at nearly ten o'clock in the evening, we sat down on the carpet and opened my birthday presents together.

Although Sally felt much better the next day, she duly phoned the Early Pregnancy Unit and told them everything which the hospital consultant had told us. However, they explained that it was too early to carry out a scan as nothing would show up yet. Their advice was to keep a close eye on the situation and to phone back if Sally experienced any significant pains or bleeding. Sal phoned them back on Thursday as she had been spotting all day Wednesday and was naturally quite concerned. The lady (who was apparently very nice) explained the possible reasons for this and that, unfortunately, it was still too early to see much on a scan. They said that, if Sally did start to bleed heavily or experience severe one-sided pain or shoulder-tip pain then she should get in touch straight away as this would likely be a sign that something was wrong with the pregnancy.

In the mean time, the best approach was to monitor what was happening, take it a few days at a time, and phone back on Christmas Eve when they would be able to book her in for a scan later that week.

I could see that this was having a draining affect on Sal. She was notably more lethargic than normal, even when it came to doing festive things for Christmas (which she loves). She cancelled her haircut appointment, backed out of meeting up with her fellow teachers for their end-of-term bash and even decided to give her beloved 'Carols Around the Christmas Tree' a miss this year (although it was lashing it down with rain). It was clear that she believed this pregnancy was not meant to be.

Indeed, she told me that the body is pre-programmed to get rid of pregnancies that aren't 'right' and that whatever happens, it will be for the best.

Sal's mum and heavily pregnant sister Clare both told her that they experienced bleeding and discomfort during their pregnancies. However, this was all to no avail as Sally had by now convinced herself that things were not going to end well.

4

If last week was a roller-coaster then it is fair to say that this week has been a full-scale rocket launch. Sally was still spotting at the beginning of the week so she phoned the Early Pregnancy Unit on Christmas Eve and booked an appointment for an ultrasound scan on Friday.

However, at around 2am on the morning of the scan, she got a call on her mobile from Clare (the sister who was due to drop). Things were 'happening' and she needed to get to the hospital. Unfortunately her ever-thoughtful boyfriend John was unable to drive her there as he had treated himself to a few too many pints of bitter while playing poker at his local pub that evening. Being one of Clare's two designated 'birthing partners', Sally rushed round to their house, picked the two of them up and went straight to the hospital. The next thing I know, it's 9.30 in the morning and my mobile is beeping with the message that Sal is still with Clare and John at the hospital and the baby has yet to make an appearance, therefore I should meet her there for our ultrasound appointment at 11.35am.

I duly arrived at around 11.20am and met up with Sal outside the Women and Child Unit where she had been keeping Clare company all night in the labour suite upstairs. Apparently, she was ready to blow but Sal wanted her to keep a lid on it until she could get back up there and witness the magic for herself.

Sal seemed quite upbeat as we sat in the Outpatients waiting area, although I assumed this may have been a by-product of the adrenaline she had been experiencing upstairs. After a very short wait, we were called through to the ultrasound suite where two very enthusiastic ladies went to great lengths to put Sally at ease as she positioned herself accordingly on the bed. I sat on a chair next to the bed and held Sal's hand as one of the ladies poured an almost comically large amount of sticky gel onto her belly.

The mood in the room seemed to change at that moment. The first lady positioned the scanning device on Sally's belly and then looked at her monitor, which was purposely positioned so that we couldn't see it. The second lady then came and stood by the shoulder of the first and stared intently at the screen in front of her. The first lady said: 'I just want to look at something before I show you...' and then her voice trailed off. She pressed some buttons on the elaborate looking keyboard in front of her and scrolled the scanner back and forth across Sal's lower abdomen.

She said 'I just want to check something else before I show you...' but again left her sentence unfinished.

The two ladies made brief comments to each other which meant nothing to me or Sal, and which didn't give away anything regarding what they were seeing. For a brief moment, I wondered if they too enjoyed playing poker. Finally, the two of them seemed to agree on something and that gave the first lady the impetus to turn the monitor around so that we could see it.

'Do you see this tiny image here?' she said pointing to a flickering blue blot that looked to me like a flashing cursor key on an old Commodore 64 boot-up screen.

'That's the baby's heartbeat'.

Now I like to think of myself as being quite a stoic, old-school type of guy; but at that moment I felt a warmness run through my insides that had me welling up like Paul Gascoigne circa 1990. I looked at Sal and saw a beautiful smile on her face that seemed to perfectly encapsulate how I was feeling inside.

A heartbeat.

The second of the two ladies exclaimed 'I'm so pleased' and gave a muted couple of claps to show just how pleased she was.

I looked at the monitor, transfixed. The first lady told us some measurements and confirmed the pregnancy as being around six weeks and six days. That's a heartbeat I thought to myself. That's a human being inside Sal which wasn't there seven weeks ago. How can that be?

The two ladies talked some more and told us that the pregnancy looked fine and that nothing appeared to be overtly abnormal.

I was of course thrilled as this immediately evaporated the mist of cancerous thoughts that had been silently gathering in both mine and Sal's minds whilst we dutifully played board games and pretended all was well over Christmas.

A heartbeat. A baby. My baby. Holy shit!!

And then Sal's mobile beeped.

Clare had popped!!

Yes, John and Clare's wee bonny lad Finley had finally decided to take the short bungee jump out of his mummy's nice, warm tummy just as me and Sal were finishing up our ultrasound appointment. Any disappointment Sal may have had of missing the magic moment upstairs in the labour suite must have been very short-lived as she was absolutely beaming as we made our way out of the Outpatients area on the ground floor. I could feel that, after a week or two of feeling really quite helpless and wretched, she literally radiated with positivity.

As did I.

Our baby was fit and healthy, Clare and John's baby was finally here AND the hospital car parks were free all day.

Truly it was a great day to be alive!

After a celebratory hug and kiss, Sal bounced up the stairs of the Women and Child Unit to introduce herself to her new nephew while I made my way back to the car park with my gratis ticket. I was forbidden from joining her as I was not a 'designated birthing partner' and therefore did not have the medical vetting, security clearance or character references which all well meaning visitors seemingly need to get anywhere near a maternity ward these days...

Nevertheless, I was feeling elated, not only for me and Sal, but also for Clare and John. They too had been trying for a child for a long time so the arrival of a healthy baby boy really had been a long time coming for them. This feeling stayed with me all day, from the drive home right through to when Sal arrived back late in the afternoon. It was a very simple feeling of contentment, kind of like that of waking up in the morning as a kid and seeing the garden all covered in snow. Lovely.

When Sal did finally come through the door just before tea time, she was tired but effervescently happy. So we kicked back with a nice cup of tea, sprawled out on the sofas in the living room, and revelled in our new found contentment. After a while however, Sally pointed out that, whilst the scan was indeed good news, it in no way guaranteed all would be well. She went on to say that miscarriages can occur any time within the first 23 weeks of a pregnancy, so we really shouldn't consider ourselves 'out of the woods' just yet.

Whist I knew this was of course true, it didn't seem to apply to us right at that moment. All I knew was I'd seen evidence Sal had a living, breathing (?) baby-type thing in her belly which experienced professionals had identified as being 'Okay'.

And that was more than enough for me.

5

So we went round to see Clare, John and baby Finley a couple of days after the wee man had arrived. Weighing in at just over seven pounds, Finley is perhaps the smallest human being I have ever seen in my life. In fact, Smudge (our cat) is probably bigger than he is.

However, seeing him there on his changing mat, having his backside wiped by Clare in a rather unceremonious way, completely blew my mind. I just couldn't get to grips with the fact that, two days ago, he was inside Clare's belly.

And once that little existentialist nugget eventually stopped flying around my head, I started reflecting on the fact that, nine or so months ago, Finley didn't exist at all. There was no Finley - no arms, no legs, no thatch of black hair – nothing.

How can this be?

Now I am in no way a religious person but I can see why so many people regard the birth of a baby as being something of a miracle.

I couldn't help but dwell on this as Sally held the tiny little fella in her arms. He is a living, breathing, fully aware life-form – a person in his own right. He has his whole life ahead of him yet, at this moment in time, he has absolutely no concept of anything other than being hungry, tired and dirty. The only thing that brought me out of this really quite pleasant introspectiveness was a slightly heavy smell that parked itself under my nose. As a man, I instinctively made the wafting motion with my left hand and gave a slightly over exaggerated 'phwoar' as I looked accusingly at Finley.

Sally looked at me, sheepishly.

'That was me', she said. 'Pardon'.

To be fair, Finley didn't seem too bothered by Sally's poorly timed attempts to replicate mustard gas; however, it did seem like the appropriate time for me to give him a cuddle.

Now, if I'm being totally honest, I have never really felt comfortable holding babies. I don't know why this is but I have always been somewhat reluctant to take my turn whenever a baby was being passed around for cuddling duties at social gatherings. Maybe it is because I have lacked any kind of natural paternal instinct in the past. Or, maybe it is because I have been frightened of dropping them. Most likely, it was just because I found the whole 'coochy-coochy-coo' thing to be just a little bit irritating.

Yet, here I was holding young Finley in my arms, stroking his inordinately hairy head almost automatically and cradling him so close that not even one of Sally's bean-heavy farts could pose a threat to him. Sure, he wriggled around a little bit and let forth a little yelp every now and then, but eventually, he settled down and seemed quite content to just lie there. Lie there and make strange little pouting gestures.

The four of us continued talking and no-one seemed too fussed that here was I, a once self-confessed loather of children, looking for all the world like a grown up, caring father-to-be. And you know what? It felt really quite nice.

But then John decided to step it up a gear. 'D'ya want to feed him Mr C?' he said in his gentle Glaswegian lilt.

I had never fed a baby in my life. More to the point, I didn't even know if my nipples would produce milk.

He produced a bottle.

'Sure, why not?' I replied, feeling buoyed by Finley's eventual acceptance of me being his new, all-time favourite cuddle partner.

So, with a little bit of guidance from John and some strategic to-ing and fro-ing with the bottle on my part, the wee man eventually suckled onto the teat and gobbled down his milk in much the same way as his dad gobbles down John Smith's when he's playing poker.

I was feeding a baby!

It felt odd to think that I would be doing this with my own child in around eight months time. When Finley was about half way through his bottle, John told me that Finley would need to be burped. 'What does that involve?' I said

'It's easy. You just need to sit him up and support him with one hand, and then rub his back with your other hand until he burps up a bit of goo'.

I handed him back to Sal.

Even Sally, who has looked after countless children over the years, seemed a little wary of holding such a small baby in a position which looked too contrived to be good for one so young. However, she did it and eventually the little guy delivered a tiny little belch which was, fortunately for Sal, free of goo. However, about five seconds after Finley had returned to his favoured supine position, another fetid smell reached my nose.

'Both ends?' I ventured.

'Nope' said Sal. 'Me again'.

Classy.

A few days later I started thumbing through some of the pregnancy books Clare had kindly given us after we had left her and her first born chewing on Sally's air biscuits. Understandably, these books are written very much with women in mind and as such I initially found them quite easy to put down.

However, through a mixture of genuine curiosity and serendipitous guilt, I persevered with one or two of the more accessible offerings and eventually settled into a nice bit of semi-laboured page turning. An hour or so later, I'd finished yet another chapter and realised I had read the best part of 100 pages.

Wow!

Although I had not read every page in the greatest of detail (I skipped right past 'aromatherapy essentials'), the information I did take in convinced me of two things:

1. That women have a LOT to worry about when they're pregnant, and:

2. That I am nowhere near as knowledgeable as I need to be.

I had concluded that knowing about spotting, trimesters and ectopic pregnancies was enough to earn me a Champion's League spot in the Premier League of pregnancy knowledge. How wrong I was.

There really is SO much more going on than I had appreciated. For example, I have noticed how Sally has become noticeably more tired over the last few weeks. She now limits herself to three locations in the home: the bed, the living room sofa - complete with furry blanket - and the toilet (we live in a bungalow so the toilet is conveniently located exactly half-way between the living room sofa and the bed).

Now I'm smart enough to know that incubating a baby inside you must be tiring work so I expected Sal to be a bit lethargic every now and then. However, it has now got to the point where I need to have her sofa blanket ready for her when she comes home from work (so she doesn't have to reach for it), and have *The Chase* on the telly ready for her when she gets in (so that she doesn't have to cope with the stress of pressing the heavy buttons on the television remote).

Before I read these books, I thought Sal might be milking this fatigue lark just a tiny, little bit, like she does whenever she's feeling poorly (she's a proper 'woe is me' whenever she catches a cold). But, now that I know her body is building our baby's limbs, organs, eye lids and tail (tail? WTF??), and creating its essential life-supporting placenta, I'm in a mind to think differently. Moreover, she has to do all this while maintaining a robust immune system and creating enough energy to work four days of the week in a busy primary school.

I feel like a proper class A bastard. I should never have doubted her. Another thing I have found out is that pregnant women's poo travels much slower than the super-efficient faeces which glides so effortlessly through unburdened women. The reason for this is that increased levels of progesterone causes the muscles in the digestive tract to relax, thereby slowing intestinal activity and making the poo hard. As well as leading to uncomfortable constipation, this can also cause ladies who are with child to experience more frequent bouts of flatulence.

The penny had dropped: Sally was not – as I had unfairly labelled her at the time – 'a grotty trumper', she was just a woefully poor expeller of shit.

Bless her.

6

My Mum absolutely adores children. Indeed, she has told me repeatedly that the only thing she ever wanted to be when she was growing up was a Mum. Some girls wanted to be nurses, some girls wanted to be Mrs Paul McCartney: my Mum wanted only to be a mum.

And of course, she got her wish.

Now, with me all grown up, all she wants is to be a grandmother.

When I told her a year and a half ago that Sal and I were trying for a baby she was absolutely ecstatic. In retrospect, it was a mistake to tell her then as that was before I found out I had an abnormally low sperm count. In the weeks and months that followed, my Mum would start every single phone conversation with an enthusiastic enquiry of 'Any news?' I would tell her 'No; nothing yet' and 'It's not for a lack of trying'.

One night, not that long ago, she started our weekly phone conversation in the same way as previous outings. She asked her standard question and I gave one of my standard answers in much the same way as spies exchange coded messages when they meet for the first time. However, on this particular evening, my mum didn't retort with her usual small talk. She instead paused, inhaled deeply and came back with:

'Maybe you should get some tests done?'

Unbeknownst to my Mum, Sally and I had already got some tests done. Sally had been through a whole load of fertility assessments, while I had been asked to do just one test – a semen analysis test.

This basically involved ejaculating into a plastic container and then getting it to the hospital lab within an hour so that the sample could be accurately analysed. Both Sally and I completed what was asked of us and waited for the results.

Sally's came back clear. Mine didn't.

Whilst the volume and mobility of my sperm was fine, the actual number of healthy sperm in my semen was low. Woefully low, in fact.

In order to conceive, the average man should have at least 15% healthy sperm. My results showed I had 3%.

'Yes, you really ought to get some tests done' she

reiterated. 'Maybe you're firing blanks?' I gave a half-hearted laugh as if to say 'Me? Blanks? You must be joking!'

This really was a different kind of pain. My own Mum half-mocking me when I was feeling about as emasculated as it's possible for a man to feel. I felt absolutely dire. And, for some reason, very alone. Anyway, the conversation went on and I did my best to not sound like a man who had just had his innards ripped out. Not long after we exchanged goodbyes, I went and laid in the bath for about an hour before heading straight to bed.

Fast forward a week and the phone is ringing at the same time on Sunday evening as it always does.

'Hello?'

'It's meeee' says my Mum, completely unnecessarily.

'No?' I said. And so we go through it.

Pleasantries out of the way, I get ready for the inevitable. However, after two minutes of chatting she has yet to enquire about anything other than the weather and our cat's health. Five minutes in and still nothing; not even a hint at what may or may not be happening in the baby-making department. Eventually we say goodbye. Nothing. The next week is the same. The week after that too. No enquiries, no mention of babies.

She knew. I don't know how she knew, but I knew she knew.

Three months after my first semen test, I took another one (apparently it takes three months for a man to generate new sperm). As per the instructions given by our Mary

Poppins-esque fertility consultant, Sister Wendy, I had got into the habit of taking male supplements during the intervening three months and stopped taking super-hot baths (which I love) and wearing tight-fitting underwear. In short, I was feeling optimistic that the results of my second test would be much better than the first.

And they were.

Sadly, they were still woefully low. The percentage of healthy sperm in my semen had risen to 6%. Normally a 100% improvement is cause for celebration. In this case however, it still left me far short of where I needed to be.

I remember feeling quite sick when I was told this.

After going through the semen test results with us, Sister Wendy told us all about the wonders of IVF, what we would be entitled to on the NHS and which of our local clinics had the best success rates. To her credit, she made it sound like the perfect solution and that we'd be able to benefit from it in as little as six months if our 'situation' didn't change.

To me, the situation was quite clear.

Sally, who was clearly 100% healthy and ready to have a baby, was in the unfortunate situation of being stuck in a relationship with a jaffa who didn't have any lead in his pencil. Unsurprisingly, this played on my mind a lot. I began to think that maybe Sally would be better off without me. She was talking about the virtues of IVF and how we would still find the money for further treatment even if it didn't happen on the NHS first time around. Meanwhile I was thinking: 'Why should a healthy girl of 34 have to waste her time plucking at 'maybes' with me when she could be getting pregnant the natural way with a man who is actually capable of doing what real men are meant to do?'

I thought hard about it over the next week or so. Eventually I concluded that the best course of action would be to leave Sally if the NHS IVF treatment didn't work. Rather than getting loans to pay for something that had a relatively slim chance of being successful, I would start acting like a complete dickhead and make her hate me, that way she could kick me out without feeling any guilt and find someone else who would be able to give her the family she so desperately wanted.

At the time this seemed like a good idea.

It would surely turn me into a bitter old man, but I couldn't bear the thought of Sally watching all her friends and family bringing up their kids while she had nothing but a cat and a man she would surely come to resent to look after. At that time, it made a lot of sense. Of course, this whole contingency plan got shelved ten weeks ago when Sally woke me up waving a magic pen in my face.

And words really can't describe just how grateful I am for that.

My Mum phoned this week, enquiring as to how Finley was getting on. I told her all about the wee man and she cooed and aahed in that way mothers do whenever they hear about things like baby mittens and Moses baskets. Once she had heard enough of Finley's quite predictable adventures, she asked how Sally and I were getting on at making a baby of our own. She hadn't asked for a while so I was a little taken aback.

After a brief pause, which I don't think she picked up on, I eventually told her that we were 'Still trying...'

7

Aside from the first 48 hours after finding out Sally was pregnant, I have genuinely experienced no real doubts regarding whether or not I am ready to become a dad. In fact, it would be fair to say I've embraced the idea of it all quite wholeheartedly and haven't really experienced any kind of niggling doubts at all.

Until now that is.

I don't know why, but something has changed within me during this last week. It hasn't been caused by any kind of trigger or unleashed by any particular event as far as I can tell – it just seems to have 'come on' somehow.

The best way I can describe it is that it feels like the novelty of it all (so to speak) has just kind of drifted away; that the honeymoon period has come to an end.

Is this normal?

For the past two months I have genuinely enjoyed my persistent daydreams of playing football over the park with my son or watching *The Snowman* at Christmas with my daughter. Indeed, I have been very happy for musings like these (and a hundred others besides) to monopolise my thoughts for the past nine or so weeks. This last week however, I feel as though another side of my psyche is trying to put some kind of counter-argument across. Now

I don't want it to sound like I've done a complete U-turn on the idea – that is not the case. I just feel as though I've been enjoying some kind of rose-tinted, one-dimensional view of becoming a father and have now been forced to accept there are other things to consider.

Things like 'Do I really want this? I mean, REALLY want this?' I think I do. I mean I'm pretty sure I do. But after two months of being completely and utterly 100 per cent, 90-odd per cent feels very inadequate.

Of course, it's possible that I'm just having a bit of a downer. I can be quite a moody so-and-so at times (ask anyone who knows me) and it is certainly not unknown for me to wallow in my own melancholy for a few days at a time. However, I have been feeling this way for the best part of a week now and it doesn't feel like it's going to shift any time soon. I tried reading some of Sal's pregnancy books to see if they might provide me with some insight. I hoped that delayed doubts might be a common reaction of fathers-to-be and that the books would tell me I am right on schedule ('Week 11 – baby's head is half the size of its body and father-to-be craps himself'). Sadly there was no mention of it (well, they are written from the expectant mother's point of view after all).

I was even feeling this way when Clare, John and Finley came round a couple of days ago. Clare and John were cool (they seem to have taken this whole parenting thing right in their stride) but young Finley was grizzling quite a bit. My theory was that the bear-type romper suit (complete with ears) they had dressed him in was upsetting him - he knew he looked like a twat. Regardless of whether it was down to his choice of outfit or boredom brought on by his rather mundane routine of pooing, drinking and sleeping; he was clearly having an 'off day'. I felt no compulsion to pick him up and no urge to try and calm him down. In fact, the only urge I did have was to feign illness, get shot of them all and have my living room back to being a peaceful haven again. But why? I didn't have the answers three days ago and I don't have them now. All I know is that I just don't feel as 'in to it' as I did last week and that is making me question everything.

Sal has picked up on this. I think she feels her general lack of motivation (and energy) to do anything is what is getting me down. If I'm being honest, it's not helping matters. Indeed I feel like a housewife most days; cleaning up, washing up, putting tea on and making sure everything is ready for her when she gets in. I used to think of myself as being something of a man of action; an alpha male – now I feel about as manly as Mrs Doyle in *Father Ted*!

Of course, Sally isn't really to blame for anything. I try to reassure her that she's not the reason why I may seem less excited about things this week but I don't think she believes me. Naturally, I won't burden her with this unwelcome development. Rather, I think the best thing to do is to wait and see if these doubts fade away as mysteriously as they appeared

Needless to say, there's no Plan B so I hope they do.

8

Unfortunately, little seems to have changed for me over the last week as I still feel somewhat out of sorts. I still don't know for sure why this is; however, I am beginning to think (hope) that it is not so much a fear of becoming a dad as it is just a lull in mine and Sal's relationship. Of course, all relationships ebb and flow. Sometimes couples feel like they fit together like a hand in a glove, and other times they feel about as compatible as a foreskin and a zip-fly. It could just be that Sal and I are experiencing a bit of a collective 'downer' at this particular moment in time.

I say this because the easy going, super-positive euphoria that has been evident for much of the past month-or-so is quite conspicuous by its absence now. Tension currently seems to be the predominant ambience hovering around our little bungalow now, and not a volatile, waiting-to-combust-type of tension where the least little thing will set off an almighty row, but rather a festering, gradual build up of pressure which seems to hang around like an ill dog's fart.

The thing is, I knew that something like this was likely to happen. Indeed, the first-hand accounts recorded by pregnant women in Sal's pregnancy books informed me that expectant mothers don't just feel tired around the 10 – 14 week mark; they also feel snappy and are (apparently) helpless to stop themselves from being unreasonable. Despite being forewarned however, Sally's lethargy and impatience have crept up and infiltrated my defences. I know she is incubating our baby and having to deal with all manner of things which I have absolutely no way of empathising with, but sometimes I forget this when she comes home to a spotless house, drops her work things all over the floor and tells me she's not really in the mood for the food I've prepared for tea. It's also hard to take a step back and remember what she's going through when she asks me to fetch her yet another drink of cordial, put her box of school books in the car, feed the cat, set the heating and put the bin out while she just lies there under her furry blanket all evening watching *Don't Tell the Bride.*

I know she's tired and I know her body's working overtime; but sometimes I feel more like a live-in-carer than a boyfriend. Of course, it probably isn't as bad as it come across in print, and Sal has apologised at times. However, I am only human and can't always separate myself from my feelings – even when the experts in the books say I ought to.

In truth, I am hoping that the scan we are due to have next week will change things a bit and put some positivity back into proceedings.

The 12-week scan (the Nuchal Fold Ultrasound to be more accurate) is actually a bit of a landmark event in the first trimester as it not only provides peace of mind that the foetus has survived the most likely time to miscarry; it also gives an idea as to whether or not a child is liable to have Down's Syndrome.

Naturally, Sal and I have spoken about what the 'best' course of action would be if it was determined our baby had a high chance of being born with Down's Syndrome. I had considered this situation before Sal fell pregnant and was pretty sure I knew where I stood on the subject. But, when we were actually talking about it aloud, discussing it with the 'Bump' in the room as it were, it seemed a lot more macabre somehow and so my thoughts became much more clouded. To discuss whether or not a child gets to live or not in such a matter of fact way made me feel a bit like a Nazi talking over the finer points of the Final Solution.

After what seemed like a very, very long time we eventually agreed that – for us at least - it would probably be better not to proceed with such a pregnancy. And then we didn't speak of it again.

Of course, if everything goes well with the scan, I will finally be able to tell my Mum and Dad (and everyone else) that Sal is expecting. Although Sally's mum, step-dad, sisters and close friends know she is pregnant, I have yet to tell anyone on my side of the family (or friends of mine who know my family) our news. The main reason for this is that my Mum suffers bouts of pretty severe anxiety at times. Therefore, I want to be as sure as I can that the good news I will give her is likely to stay good news.

Without doubt, the prospect of a new grandchild arriving would give my Mum a boost of positivity that no amount of Diazepam could even begin to match. In fact, it wouldn't be an understatement to suggest it might give her a whole new lease of life. But, if I gave her unbelievably good news like that and then had to follow it some time later with a sentence that started with 'the doctors say something isn't quite right...', I think it would absolutely destroy her. To get her hopes up and then bring them tumbling down in such a fashion would be a truly crushing blow from which she might not recover. So, it is fair to say there is actually quite a bit resting on this scan. If it goes well then I will probably invite my Mum and Dad up soon after and take enormous delight in giving them the good news. You never know, their nuclear-powered enthusiasm may well give Sal and I the shot in the arm we seem to need right now.

If the scan shows us there is some kind of problem however... well; we'll cross that bridge if and when we come to it.

9

Sally and I went for the Nuchal Fold Scan on Tuesday afternoon and thankfully had a far more straightforward experience than the last time we went for a scan. After a bit of a prolonged wait, we eventually went into the Antenatal Ultrasound Room and assumed our respective positions (Sally on the bed, me on the chair next to her) without waiting to be prompted. Unlike the ultrasound room of the Early Pregnancy Unit, there was a monitor hanging from the ceiling at the end of the bed so we'd both be able to see what was happening this time without trying to second guess the operators. There was just one 'scanner person' (I don't know their official title) for this appointment; a very chilled out lady whose whole persona simply exuded confidence and competence.

As before, a large wad of gel was deposited on Sal's belly and as before my hand reached up automatically to stroke her head. The monitor at the end of the bed (which looked to me like the ideal solution for playing video games when you're unwell) sparked into life and immediately began to relay images that looked like they should be more familiar than they were.

Mrs Scanner gave us a peppered commentary:

'There's the head; there's the legs; there's an arm – look baby's waving'.

'Ahhh'.

'Now baby's turned his back and rolled over'

'Ohhh'.

I looked at Sal and she was smiling.

'It's weird isn't it?' she said. 'It's really in there!'

It's true; it did feel a bit weird. The flashing little blip we had seen five weeks ago was now a recognisable human form, with legs, arms and hands – alive and well. It also seemed quite unsociable and keen to be left alone. I took this as a sign that he was definitely a boy (although I kept this to myself).

'I'm just going to take a few measurements now' said Mrs Scanner as she simultaneously moved the scanning wand around Sally's abdomen with one hand and clicked a few buttons on her keyboard with the other. Little interchangeable vectors and squares flashed up on the monitor in much the same way as those lines do whenever you're trying to make your documents look a little more arty-farty in MS Word. I looked at the image more closely to see if I could see any obvious abnormalities for myself. After a few strained sweeps however, it was clear that my untrained eyes weren't going to give me any kind of advanced warning as to whether or not the kid was out of proportion in any way. In truth, he could have had a nose like Pinocchio and I would have been none the wiser.

During this hiatus, I gave Sal a reassuring stroke and asked if she was OK. 'Fine' she said; and she was. I think the fact we had already experienced our first visual encounter with 'bump' made this scan a far less emotional affair than the one before. Although I was genuinely amazed to see the images on the screen, the experience didn't have the same 'Oh my God' resonance that was so evident during the first scan. Sally clearly felt the same way. After a bit of deliberating, Mrs Scanner eventually said:

'Well, everything seems normal'. Sal and I looked at each other yet said nothing. All was well.

'Of course, we won't be able to give you any estimates regarding Down's Syndrome until the blood work comes back' she continued, 'But nothing I've seen today has given me cause for concern'.

I liked Mrs Scanner. She was brief, articulate and to the point. I imagined Mr Scanner was probably a very happy man. 'Here are your scans' she said as she put two photos into two separate presentation wallets and deposited them into Sal's already bulging maternity file/MI6 dossier. This was then put into her even more cavernous 'Bounty Pack'/Al-Qaeda case file.

'You'll need to pay for them at the machine in the corridor'. I immediately went off Mrs Scanner. At least Dick Turpin wore a mask.

A few days later we got a letter in the post which contained the results of the blood tests Sal had done straight after the scan. Sally opened the envelope and read aloud:

"...I am sure you will be pleased to hear that your recent maternal screening test has shown that your baby is not at high risk for Down's Syndrome."

She looked up at me and inhaled. "We have combined the results of your blood test with the result of your nuchal scan to calculate the chance of Down's Syndrome in your pregnancy. The results show that your chance of having a baby with Down's Syndrome is:

1 in 2000

This means that out of every **2000** women with the same result as you, **one** will have a baby with Down's Syndrome, and **1999** will have unaffected babies."

'One in 2,000' repeated Sal. 'I'm sure Clare's odds were higher than that!'

Sal re-read the letter. 'Yes. I'm positive Clare had something like 1 in 10,000 when she got her letter'. I knew what was coming next.

'I'm going to phone Clare'.

1 in 2,000 sounded pretty good to me, after all the odds of dying from a slip in the bathroom are about the same and I don't know of anyone who's kicked the bucket by taking a tumble in the shower. Moreover, 1 in 2,000 equates to 0.05% when it is translated to a percentage – pretty good odds, I thought..

I could hear Sal on the phone '...That's what I thought. No, I think Leanne's was 1 in 600'. I don't get it; you're older than me..?' And so it went on for another five or ten minutes.

The way I saw it, there was nothing we could do about the odds we had been given. Sal however, being one of three sisters growing up in a household of five children, needed to process these statistics by scrutinising them with good old-fashioned sibling rivalry rather than opting for the highly overrated merits of logic and reason.

'...What was Tina's? Really? I'm going to phone Mum...'

After a little while, my patience ran out so I sat Sally down and gave her the Brian Clough treatment. Namely, we talked about it for 20 minutes and then we decided I was right. Amazingly, this seemed to work. The truth is, nature doesn't abide by odds so it really didn't matter if our chances of having a baby with Down's were better than Leanne's or worse than Clare's – what would be, would be. And, the fact that the letter had stated our pregnancy was not regarded as 'high risk' was surely enough to be going on with.

After a few hours of me working in the spare room and Sally milling about on the laptop in the living room, she eventually popped her head round the door. 'Shall we invite your Mum and Dad up tomorrow?' she asked. 'Now would be a good time to tell them, don't you think?'

I leaned back in my chair and thought about it. The scan revealed nothing worrying and Sally had not experienced any bleeding or associated pains in weeks.

'If we wait much longer to tell them, they'll see I'm pregnant before we get the chance to announce it nicely'.

I considered this and weighed it all up. My Mum and Dad would want to receive this news in person and now did 'feel' like the right time to do it. 'Okay' I said 'I'll give her a call'.

Sally beamed a smile: 'This news will make her year'. I smiled back: 'It'll make her decade'.

The next day, Sal and I were playing a game of *Risk* (the classic PC version) while we waited for my Mum and Dad to arrive. There aren't many girls who are into *Risk*, and it is one of the many idiosyncrasies that Sal does like it which makes me love her. For some reason, everything seemed better again between the two of us. Here we were, kicking back on the sofa, playing games on the laptop and listening to some tunes, just like we'd done a thousand times before – and it felt just as nice as ever.

In fact, we were enjoying our game of world domination so much that we were actually a bit gutted when we saw my dad's car pull onto the drive (Sal was more gutted – she was winning). Within 90 seconds of parking on the drive, my Mum was already in the front door (she knocks yet doesn't wait for anyone to answer). 'Hellooo?' she sang. Sal and I took turns to give her a hug. She looked happy and well.

A minute later, my Dad came bounding in like Tigger from *Winnie the Pooh.* He has angina as well as a whole host of other health problems but they all seem to fade away when he comes up to visit us. He greeted me and Sal with a big smile and an infectious chuckle.

'Cup of tea?' I ventured. 'Took the words right out of my mouth' he replied, laughing.

So we sat down in the living room with our cuppas and chewed the fat for a bit. They had arranged to come up and visit around this time anyway so neither of them had any inkling of what was to come.

Rather than simply tell them the news, I instead opted to put two enlarged photos of the most recent scan pictures into an envelope with an accompanying piece of paper with 'See you in August' written on it. I left this on the fireplace in full view and waited for an opportune moment to present it to them. After a good 45 minutes of making cheerful small talk, the conversation reached a natural hiatus. This was it. This was the moment! I stood up, grabbed the envelope and told my Mum and Dad that Sal and I had a present to give them.

'Ooohh' my Mum said 'A present? For me?'

'For both of you' I corrected 'So you'll both need to sit next to each other when you open it'. Dad moved from the sofa he was sharing with me across to the bigger sofa Mum was sitting on with Sally (who duly moved to come and stand next to me). My Mum opened the envelope, tugged at the paper she found and leaned forward to read what she saw: 'See. You. In. August'

'Ooohhh, is it tickets to see Paul McCartney?' she quizzed.

Dad joined in: 'Is it a holiday?'

I shook my head. She pulled the paper out and turned the contents over to get a better view.

'Oooooooo.....ayyyyyyy....YAAAYYYYYYY!!!!!!!!'

Dad leaned across for a better view and started laughing. 'Yaaaaaayyyyyyy!!!' my Mum continued as she flicked from one image to the other: 'Oh he's beautiful. Beautiful! Look David: he's beautiful'.

'Yeah! YEAH!!' Dad said, laughing almost uncontrollably now.

My mum got to her feet and started crying as she gave me a big hug. Gently weeping, she grasped me tightly and told me how everything was brilliant. After giving Sally a big cuddle, she returned to me and sobbed as she hugged me even tighter. 'I...I feel... so...so happy' she eventually said.

My dad was misty eyed as he finally got the opportunity to congratulate me properly. He wanted to be a grandparent just as much as Mum and I could see in his eyes that this news was just as amazing for him as it was for her. It was a magic moment, one which I wish I could have frozen so that I could enjoy it over and over again. I couldn't remember the last time I had seen my Mum looking so thrilled about anything.

I felt unbelievably happy myself.

I was sharing a genuinely life-affirming moment with the three (soon to be four) most important people in my life. Everything felt perfect.

THE SECOND TRIMESTER

1

According to Sally's pregnancy books, this is the most 'comfortable' trimester of the pregnancy, where energy levels rise, nausea bouts fall and mood swings abate.

Unfortunately, the joys of the comfortable second semester have yet to hit Sal.

Sally's energy levels are now on a par with those of an elderly koala (a pregnant elderly koala at that). The living room has become something of a 'nest' and her furry blanket and pouffe have usurped Cabernet Sauvignon and *DIY SOS* as being the two most important things in her life. In fact, her blanket has become a kind of exo-skeleton which automatically envelops her like Robert Downey Jr's *Ironman* costume every time she ventures into the living room.

As well as being constantly tired, Sal has spent most of the last week being ill as well. I really do feel sorry for her as she looks so fed up as she plods from her living room nest to her bedroom retreat, sniffling and coughing into her tissues. She can't even enjoy the all-curing medicine that is the mighty Lemsip hot lemon drink as it contains ingredients which medical professionals regard as being 'potentially harmful' to foetuses.

And, as if having the flu isn't bad enough, she can't even get the rest she needs because she finds it almost impossible to get comfortable when trying to sleep at night. Apparently, sleeping on your back is another potential threat to unborn babies so she has to use pillows and cushions to force herself to try and sleep on her side. This is all to no avail though as she says her hips and knees ache so much she simply cannot stay in one position long enough to enjoy a really good sleep.

Whilst I have done all I can to make sure she is comfortable (making her hot water bottles, cooking her stodgy meals, watching lovey-dovey DVDs); there isn't much I can do to make her feel better in herself. This makes me feel bad as I don't like to see her like this; all frustrated, defeated and resigned. I can see in her face that it's all getting on top of her and yet there is nothing tangible I can do to improve her present circumstances.

Quite simply, she is pregnant, sad, ill, and fed up.

In some respects, Sally reminds me of a character in one of the DVDs we watched together recently called *What to Expect When You're Expecting*. This film follows a number of obnoxious American couples as they 'hilariously' go through the various trials and tribulations which pregnancy inevitably throws up. One of the pregnant women characters (the one who wasn't Cameron Diaz, Jennifer Lopez or the young, fit one) takes years to get pregnant and is completely overjoyed when she and her partner finally manage to conceive. Over the course of the film however, the 'unicorns and rainbows' pregnancy experience she was hoping for just doesn't materialise. Rather than feeling the radiant glow of incubating a new life and embracing this most feminine of life events, she instead feels bloated, angry and persistently full of wind. (Funnily enough I empathised fully with this character as this was exactly how I felt after watching one and a half hours of this truly painful offering.)

The parallels were there to see.

Now I'm not saying Sally was expecting an easy ride, but it's quite obvious to me that she really isn't enjoying being pregnant very much right now.

This is a shame.

It's not just because I don't like to see her unhappy that I say this is a shame. It's a shame because we have no intentions of having more than one child; therefore this will more than likely be the one and only time she gets to experience this.

I don't want to point this out to Sal as being comprehensively patronised by me is probably the last thing she needs right now. With any luck though, the illness, melancholy and tiredness will go away or at least abate to some degree over the next week or two, so that will give me more of a chance to help kick the black cloud which presently lingers over her into touch.

Hopefully, the super-duper, specially designed maternity support pillow which is winging its way to us from Amazon as we speak will play a large part in helping to achieve this. Shaped like a large number '7' this 'wonder product' (as they say on the Internet forums Sally trawls through) is meant to provide expectant mothers with all the support they need to get a good night's sleep. Getting plenty of rest will not only help Sally to fight infections and stay healthy, it will also give her the strength she needs to incubate our Bump without feeling knackered all the time. So it is fair to say that we are both awaiting the postman's knock with a fair degree of anticipation!

2

'"Wonder product" my arse!'

Sally's pillow arrived to much excitement and fanfare at the beginning of the week. In fact, Sal was so excited about it she tried it out as soon as she got in from school. After a few minutes of lying down fully clothed with what looked like the Stay Puft Marshmallow Man's old chap squeezed between her legs, I asked her how it felt.

'Well...' she paused, trying to find the right words '...It feels a bit odd', she said eventually.

'Oh, that's probably just because you're not used to it' I countered.

'Hmmn; maybe. We'll see how it goes tonight'.

And so night-time came and Sally duly arranged her many different pillows and cushions into a huddle of supportive columns and buttresses to slumber in. Eventually she managed to get herself into a position which she found relatively comfy. To me, it looked like she was making a porno with three of the Michelin Man's younger nephews, but she seemed happy enough as I turned off the bedroom light and decamped to the living room to play PlayStation at the ungodly hour of 9.30pm. The next day I asked Sally how she slept. 'Not very well' she replied. 'I just couldn't get comfortable'. I desperately wanted this super-sausage to work so I tried to put a positive spin on things.

'Maybe your body just needs to get used to sleeping with it', I offered.

'Maybe' she replied, seemingly unconvinced by my evident grasp of ergonomics and biomechanics. 'I'll give it another go tonight'.

And so, sometime around nine o'clock that evening, Sally woke up from sleeping on the living room sofa to conclude it was time for bed. After brushing her teeth and getting into her pyjamas, she again went through the rigmarole of making a little nest on her side of the bed which would undoubtedly give her the soundest night's sleep possible. As she finally got cosy, I stroked her head and asked if she was comfy.

'For now' she replied as she gave a bear-like yawn which fired a concentrated aroma of *Colgate* right in my face.

'Sweet dreams then'.

The following day, Sally stopped me before I could ask her how she had slept. 'I am aching all over, my hips absolutely wreck, my head is pounding more than ever and I am starting to get quite an uncomfortable feeling in my stomach'. I nodded thoughtfully as I took this all in. I really did want this "wonder product" to work. I wanted it to give Sal the sleep she needed to fight off her flu-like infection and feel a bit perkier again so I chose my words very carefully, took a breath and pitched my voice to reflect my deep-held belief that good would eventually come from this time of adversity. Think Tony Blair in full-on 'People's Princess' mode. 'Maybe...' I began - but Sally cut me off straight away and grabbed her maternity pillow, pointing to it like it was damning evidence in a courtroom drama.

'Maybe this crappy pillow is making me feel worse rather than better? Maybe sleeping with a big sausage between my legs isn't the best way to guarantee a decent night's sleep when your nostrils are too bunged up to even breathe? Maybe I DON'T WANT TO SLEEP WITH A GIANT FUCKING SAUSAGE!!!'

Now we had a problem. The last thing Sal said – and the way she roared it with such venom - was the funniest thing I had ever heard in my entire life and therefore the urge to crack up was absolutely overwhelming. However, I got the feeling that laughing in Sally's face at this particular moment would do little to improve her less than chirpy demeanour.

This reminded me of those times at school when you heard someone fart in assembly yet had to try and stop yourself from giggling lest you would be removed by a teacher in full view of everyone (truly, there is nothing funnier than an under-the-radar school assembly guff!). So here I was, standing in front of Sal and her offending sausage, feeling much like the snorting Roman centurion in *Life of Brian* did when Michael Palin kept lisping "Bigguth Dickuth" to him over and over again.

It was no good. My eyes made contact with hers and before I knew it my nostrils were burning and I was whimpering like a discarded *X Factor* wannabee.

Sally's eyes lit up with a fire that indicated she was going to turn green and destroy everything within a half-mile radius. Duly, she raised her left arm and made a girly fist just as the muscles in my throat relented and let the full force of my pent-up guffaw out to echo around the room. Her mouth was contorted with rage as she landed her puny blow on my shoulder. I made a token gesture of trying to avoid her 'attack' but it really didn't matter – I was now at the point where I was paralysed with laughter and as such I wouldn't be able to muster any kind of reasonable reaction for the foreseeable future. Curiously, Sally started emitting staccato bursts of laughter as she tried to grab my shoulders and shake me. Her face was a weird contortion of expressions and she fired incomplete questions at me as she harmlessly tried to thump me on my now doubled-over back.

'Why are you..? What do you..? How can I..? Aaarrgghh!!' she spluttered as I reached the point where soiling myself was a distinct possibility.

Fortunately, her initial rage lamented as she quickly saw the full absurdity of the situation and let the obvious comedy of the moment get the better of her. Indeed, she too started laughing quite uncontrollably as we collapsed against the wall and eventually fell to the floor with tears streaming down our cheeks.

This was golden. Eventually, we managed to gain a measure of control and crawled up onto the bed. We laid there together for ages, still chuckling quite uncontrollably whenever one of us tried to speak. After what seemed like an absolute age, Sally turned to me with a broad smile and said: 'I've got to get up'. Not wanting this moment to end I asked her why she had to move.

'I'm not comfortable', she said.

Tears. I was in absolute tears.

3

I read in one of Sally's books this week that Bump is now 15cm long from his head to his bum. 15cm! That's as long as one of the rulers you used to get in those maths sets at school that had a compass, set square and protractor in! This didn't seem to phase Sal when I pointed it out to her. In truth, the only thing she seemed concerned about was the fact she couldn't feel Bump moving around that much.

If I had something – anything - growing inside me, I'm pretty sure it would freak me out. Without doubt, the idea of incubating another life-form; hosting something that is unable to live without siphoning my body's nutrients is something that makes me feel quite disturbed. If I sit back, shut my eyes and try to think seriously about how I would feel if I were in Sally's place, then it only takes a matter of moments for the image of that little bastard bursting out of John Hurt's stomach in *Alien* to pop into my head. But Sally; bless her - she seems quite at ease with the whole thing. What a girl.

I'm pleased to say that Sal's whole demeanour has improved markedly over the last week or so. As well as finally getting rid of her flu-like infection, she has managed to work out a system with her pillows that is enabling her to enjoy longer and more rewarding bouts of sleep.

This system involves using four standard bed pillows, one travel pillow, one memory foam pillow (cut in half) and, of course, one maternity, number seven sausage-like pillow in a whole host of positions that change throughout the night. Every time she gets up to go to the toilet (which is very, very often) she re-arranges her pillows when she gets back to suit a slightly different way of lying down. Although this is obviously a little bit convoluted, it seems to be doing the trick.

Seriously, it's nice to see Sal looking and feeling a little bit perkier. She has an absolutely lovely smile that you cannot help but warm to so seeing it beam around the place more often really does change the whole vibe of our little bungalow. Of course, I am not fooling myself into thinking the 'worst' is all done and over with. Indeed, all of the books I've read and the documentaries I've watched recently tell me that there are likely to be plenty more peaks and troughs to come in the months ahead.

But, as it is now, the mood around our little nest is actually pretty upbeat: Sally's feeling well, I'm feeling positive and we're both enjoying the idea of becoming real life, bona-fide parents. Of course, now that we are just over half way through the pregnancy, that amazing statement is set to become fact sooner rather than later. Whilst I find the idea a little bit scary at times and still question whether I have what it takes to be a good dad, I do actually feel (today anyway) that this really is the right time for this to happen to me. I feel like I want my life to change, and I feel like I want to take on a challenge that cannot be prepared for. This isn't just hyperbole written to package up this paragraph nicely - I really am genuinely ready for my life to change - and funnily enough, it actually makes me feel quite calm inside. Now, people of a spiritual nature might say that this is the seed of inner peace. They may even say that this is a kind of inner tranquillity that comes from being completely honest with who you are inside. Normally I would have a slightly sceptical quip readily available to deal with such observations; however, the fact is; I do feel as though there is a certain degree of truth in them.

I really do believe that I am at a stage of life where the things that were once incomprehensible to me – commitment, stability, responsibility – now feel natural and desirable. For example, I now feel content to be a homeowner whereas I once saw it as being nothing more than a financial burden that stopped me from travelling. Similarly, I now find the idea of being settled in the same part of the world for years to come very appealing. The idea of having a stable lifestyle where friends, family, social interests, hobbies and activities are all around me is really quite lovely. Even the idea of being responsible for someone else – a child – now feels good.

As I've mentioned before, this metamorphosis from 'lad' into 'man' has been a long time coming. And, whilst I knew it was happening (well, I knew something was happening), I didn't really realise - until now - what was really going on.

Put simply; I have grown up.

Of course, this might all look very different next week when we go for the 20 week scan as that will tell us whether we are going to have a little boy or girl. It could be that seeing Bump as a fully fledged human being for the first time, with a future that is dependent on me being a good father will be the moment the enormity of it all gets to me. The moment when all my talk of being grown up simply evaporates and I realise I have been deluding myself on an epic scale.

It could be - but I doubt it.

4

Oh where to begin.

Sally and I went for Bump's 20 week scan (also known as the Anomaly Scan) on Wednesday. Although we were back in the same room, we had a different sonographer (that's what they're called) this time; a very pleasant lady called Laura.

Anyway, we went through the now usual rigmarole of lying Sally down, slapping the gel on and looking transfixed at the ceiling-hung monitor as Laura prodded and poked Sally's belly with her ultrasound wand.

Laura was very methodical and talked us through what she was checking at each stage of the scan. It was really quite amazing. We could see Bump's spine, kidneys, bladder and brain. We could even see the blood as it entered and exited the various chambers of the heart. Truly, it was absolutely mind-blowing. I really was genuinely thrilled to see our little one in so much detail, and of course, so was Sal. We even got to see the lower part of the face up close at one point - truly, truly amazing.

Anyway, Laura kept on making her checks and measuring

various lengths and circumferences by way of her battle-planning software. She seemed satisfied about what she had seen up till then so she offered to tell us her opinion on what she thought the sex might be.

I looked at Sal, smiled a silly grin and took a breath.

'Well' Laura said, and inhaled a breath of her own: 'I think this baby is a little girl.'

BOOM!!!

Within the space of two seconds the image on the screen in front of us went from being a 20-week-old foetus to being our little girl. Sally looked over at me, knowing that I would be a little disappointed at it not being a boy. I smiled back at her knowing how thrilled she would be about it being a girl.

Right then and there, I didn't care that my kid probably wouldn't want to play football with me on PlayStation. I didn't care that I would spend most of my child's teenage years tearing my hair out worrying about predatory boys. I didn't even care that she would probably end up sharing her mother's enthusiasm for crappy Saturday night TV singing contests.

I just felt elated – completely and utterly elated. My little girl. Daddy's little girl. I felt like crying but I didn't do so. Sally was beaming too. I kissed her hand and stroked her head as Laura went about the business of double-checking her findings.

'I just want to double-check something I noticed earlier...' she said, her voice trailing off as Sal and I looked at the screen, both of us in our own little world. A little girl. Although I had made no secret of my desire to have a boy,

I must admit that the idea of having a little girl had grown on me over the previous few weeks. Little girls always look so sweet and – as far as I can tell – they seem to be better behaved than little boys.

Yeah, having a little girl was going to be just fine.

And then Laura's voice trailed back into my daydreams.

'...No: that doesn't seem quite right'. She was frowning and making an 'upside-down smile' face as she was leaning in as close as she could get to her workstation monitor. I looked up at Sal. She was looking at Laura.

'Not quite right?' I asked.

She pointed at the monitor and affected a sympathetic look.

'I noticed it earlier. You see the hand there - the left hand', she paused; 'there seems to be an...an absence of fingers'.

I felt an immediate sensation in my stomach, like it had been violently kicked in.

'Maybe she's just clenching her hand?' Sally volunteered.

'No, I don't think so' countered Laura; 'It's been like that since we started. Look' she pointed to the screen once more; 'You can see the thumb and palm clearly, but there are no fingers where you would expect them to be'. I looked at the screen and felt another sensation in my stomach; this time it was like I was on the world's fastest rollercoaster. At that moment there was a knock on the door and a young guy – a medical student - came in to get some supplies for the room he was working in next door.

Laura called him over to her workstation and asked him to give her a second opinion. 'Are you seeing what I'm seeing' she asked him. 'Hmm. Yes', he replied.

I looked at Sal and held her hand tighter. She seemed remarkably composed. Laura and her colleague talked in semi-hushed tones for a brief moment longer and then he left as quickly as he had come in.

'Right; well - I'm just going to pop out and speak to one of the consultants so why don't you clean yourself up and take a seat for a few minutes', Laura said as she handed Sally some tissues and made for the door. Sally did as she was asked and eventually slumped down into the chair next to mine. I tried to hug her as best I could but she seemed almost rigid. I practically had to pull her toward me but eventually her posture yielded enough to let me embrace her.

And so we just sat there, hugging – no tears, no answers, no clues – just looking at a fuzzy, echo-like image of our little girl and her seemingly incomplete hand on the ceiling-hung monitor.

Laura returned a couple of minutes later and gave us her brief. She told us that, although it was by no means certain, the scan appeared to show our little girl had four fingers missing from her left hand. Because of this, she had arranged for us to come back and have a repeat scan with a consultant next week - to confirm the findings.

By now I was starting to feel a little dizzy. Sally appeared to be holding it together although I could sense that she just wanted to get the hell out of there now. At the end of the brief, we asked Laura whether having no fingers might be indicative of anything else, a larger condition perhaps.
She said that all of the other findings were fine and that

there was nothing to suggest it wasn't an isolated event. However, she reiterated that the scan with the consultant could be more conclusive. Her professional tone was cracking just a little bit at this point and she dropped a few pens when she was collecting our scan photos from the printer. As we left the ultrasound room, Laura looked at me and asked if I was alright. I don't even remember what I said.

As soon as we walked through the double doors of the waiting area and into an empty corridor Sally folded into the wall next to her and erupted into tears. I held her as tight as I possibly could and encouraged her to let it all out. I felt like doing the same but I didn't. Years of being a stoic bastard will do that. After a few moments, Sally took refuge in a nearby toilet and asked me to give her a few minutes. Standing there in the corridor listening to Sal sob her heart out through the door was without doubt one of the worst feelings I have ever had in my life. This day of joy had turned into something else entirely within the space of five minutes and there was fuck all I could do or say to make it better.

Again, I felt dizzy. After a few minutes, Sally emerged looking slightly more composed - but quite incredulous.

I don't understand', she said. 'I haven't touched a drop of alcohol or eaten anything that I shouldn't have. Why? Why?'

Of course, I didn't have the answers.

After what seemed like an absolute age, we booked our appointment at reception, paid for our parking and drove away from the hospital.

To go and share our news with Sal's family.

I had left my car at Clare's house as that is where I had met up with Sal to drive onto the hospital earlier; therefore there was no way we could go back home without telling Clare what had happened. Clare could tell from our faces that something wasn't right as soon as we walked into her living room. Sally couldn't say anything so I gave Clare a rundown on what had transpired. Sally again collapsed into tears and this time it was Clare who held her tight and told her that everything would be OK. I sat down on the sofa, feeling just as numb as I had back in the ultrasound room.

Finley was lying in his chair fast asleep, oblivious to it all. As I sat there, I couldn't help but stare at the fingers on his little hands. How often do you even think about fingers? Until now I had never even considered what it would be like to live without fingers. But now, with the ultrasound images still fresh in my mind, all I could think about was how disadvantaged our little girl would be without them. Clare, herself in tears, gave me a hug and reassured me that everything would be alright.

We stayed at Clare's for a little bit and to be honest I'm glad we did. Sally idolises Clare and I think having us both there made it just a tiny bit easier for her. After about an hour, we decided to go home. Sally asked Clare if she would phone their Mum and explain the situation as she would undoubtedly be waiting for the 'good news' at home with baited breath. Sally thinks the world of her Mum but it was clear she didn't want to be re-telling this tale more than once today. Clare said she would phone her as soon as we left.

As Sal and I pulled into our road in our separate cars, I noticed a vehicle sat outside our bungalow with the headlights on. As I got further up the road I recognised the car – it belonged to Jan – Sally's Mum.

After pulling into the drive, Jan came inside with us and got the story which Clare had shared with her on the phone five minutes earlier. I knew she would be here - Sally is Jan's little girl and nothing would stop her from wanting to put her arm round her youngest daughter at such a time. Sal was far more composed now and managed to tell her Mum everything without getting so upset. Jan comforted her in a way that only mothers can and I'm sure Sally felt better for it.

Jan didn't stick around for too long as I think she sensed Sally just wasn't up for chatting about things in detail. As she gave me a little hug on her way out, I thought about my own Mum. She knew the scan was this week. What would I say to her? Should I tell her at all? Would she be able to handle it? But that would have to wait for now.

After Jan had gone, Sal and I sat on a sofa each in the quiet of our living room. For a while we just sat there, making non-descript noises and stroking our heads.

'I couldn't help but stare at Finley's fingers', Sally eventually said, shaking her head. 'You just don't even think about them, do you?'

I shook my head. After a little while of talking things through with Sal, I felt as though my mind was getting back to a more logical way of thinking. That being so, I fired up my netbook and started to look for answers. Within moments Sally was on her school laptop doing the same. When the Google search bar came up, I paused for a couple of seconds and thought about what my query should be. Eventually I typed '20 WEEK SCAN NO FINGERS' and hit ENTER.

Most of the results were from forums; I clicked on every one and read through them at speed. Before I knew it, the best part of an hour had passed and I had read countless forum posts, replies and articles about parents who had found out their babies were missing fingers when they had gone for their Anomaly Scan. In the main, everything I read was very positive. Indeed, almost all of the parents who'd posted their accounts online had told how their initial fears and disappointment evaporated when their son or daughter was finally born. Apparently, not having fingers on one hand is something which most children can adapt themselves to quite easily.

I wanted this positivity to make me feel better; make me look at things from a slightly different angle – but it didn't. I didn't want my little girl to have to adapt. I didn't want her to start off her life being disadvantaged. All I wanted was to have a little girl who would be able to do things which all kids do.

I wanted my child to be able cut up her own food, tie her own laces, and ride a bike. I wanted her to be able to hold a skipping rope, do gymnastics and play guitar. To go on fairground rides, ride a horse, drive a car...

HOW CAN SHE DO THESE THINGS – AND A HUNDRED OTHER BLOODY THINGS BESIDES - IF SHE'S ONLY GOT ONE FUCKING HAND THAT WORKS PROPERLY!!!

I turned the netbook off and lied down on the sofa for a while. Sally had turned her laptop off five or ten minutes earlier and had put the telly on to distract her thoughts. I suddenly felt stifled, angry. It was a good time to go for a walk. I walked the same ten-minute route as I did most days; round the block, through the local park and back up the other end of the road.

As I walked through the large, tree-fringed park of mostly

open fields, I looked across the bumps and moguls of the BMX track to the kiddies play park beyond. On previous walks, I had imagined my child playing happily on the swings, slides, trim-trail and other bits of play apparatus. When I looked at the equipment on this walk though, empty and abandoned at this time of the evening, I thought only about which of the swings and climbing frames my little girl would actually be able to use.

And it made me cry.

An hour or so later the phone rang. My Mum. I hesitated as Sally held it out for me. Reluctantly I took it and answered.

'Helloooo', she cooed, 'It's meeee!'

I really, really wasn't in the mood for this.

'Hello Mum', I said, 'How are you?'

And so she went on to tell me about her weekend and asked me irreverent questions about holidays and the weather. She had forgotten. Thank God. Whilst walking in the park I had decided that I would tell my mum the news – but only if she asked. I had concluded that telling her after the next scan would be the better option as I would be armed with more information then. And so she rambled on, telling me about her trip to the cinema and asking what our plans were for Easter. The conversation was coming to its natural end and I was glad to be doing everything I could to help it on its way.

'Oh; but what about your scan? When is that? Tomorrow? Next week? I went to speak but nothing came out. I took a deep breath and tried again.

'Today, Mum. The scan was today'.

'Oooo – did you find out what it is? Did you find out?'

'Yeah, we found out Mum; it's a girl.'

'Yaaaayyyyyy...!!!!' I moved the phone away from my ear a little as she went through every note in the scale a pensioner can hit and stamped her feet in utter delight. After about 15 seconds, I eventually returned the phone to my ear and resumed the conversation.

'Oh, I'll have to go out and buy some girls clothes now! Is that alright? Can I get some more bits for her?'

Given that my Mum and Dad bought two full bags of baby clothes and soft toys up with them the last time they came, I wanted to tell her to hold fire for a little while. But I didn't. I just wanted this phone call to end before it got to the point where I would be forced to tell her what had happened.

'OK Mum', I said 'But don't go mad, alright'

'Ooooo! A girl. A girl!

It was nice to hear her so happy. I really, really didn't want to spoil her moment so I endeavoured to get out while the going was good. 'Yeah. It's been a bit of a big day though so I'm actually quite...'

'What could you see on the scan', she said, cutting me off before I could even tell her how tired I was.

'Well. You could see everything. Her spine, her brain, her heart. You could even see the bottom of her face'.

I enjoyed telling her this. It already felt like an eon ago for me but it felt good to give her a taste of the happiness Sally and I had experienced just a few short hours ago. 'Oh, it sounds wonderful', she purred 'And you could see everything?'

'Everything' I replied, now resigned to the fact that this conversation was destined not to end on a high.

'So everything was alright, was it?'

And there it was. Just six little words - but right there and then – they seemed to have the destructive power of Krakatau and Hiroshima rolled into one. There was no way out - I had to tell her.

'Actually Mum, they think there may be a little problem with one of her hands'

I knew this would turn my Mum's guts inside out so I tried to make it seem less dramatic to her than it did to me and Sal less than four hours ago. I gave her an abridged version of what had happened at the hospital and reassured her that the scan we are due to have next week could yet yield some good news. I also told her that not developing fingers on one hand is actually quite a common occurrence (1 in every 30,000 – 40,000 babies in actual fact) and that there are of course plenty of worse things that can happen to an unborn child.

'Oh, bless her little heart' she said.

I went on to tell her that we live in a world where things like grafting and transplants are commonplace so it's not like she would be short of options. 'Yes', Mum agreed; 'they can do wonders these days'.

At that moment I heard my Dad come in to the room. My mum again got a little excited; 'It's a girl David!'
'Aaayyy!!!'

'But she might have something wrong with her hand'

'Oh...'

I had now reached my limit. I really did feel tired now and all I wanted was to make this day end so that a new one could begin. And so I wrapped things up as gently as I could, told my Mum I would phone her when I knew more and told her not to worry. I ended the call by saying; 'It's not the end of the world, Mum – it's just a little unexpected; that's all.'

And that seemed to sum things up nicely at that point

Fatigue had got the better of me and Sal by now so we decided to get an early night. To say it had been a long day would be a massive understatement. Unsurprisingly, I didn't get much sleep that night. Although I felt physically drained when I went to bed, my mind was awash with thoughts about what my little girl would and wouldn't be able to do with her left hand.

The most upsetting thought of all was knowing she would almost certainly get teased when she reached a certain age. It is human nature for children to mock or fear what they don't understand so it would eventually transpire that my little girl would have to put up with other kids calling her names. I tormented myself with this thought – and many other similar ones – for most of the night. How would she deal with this kind of teasing? What would she do when a teacher asked her class to count on their fingers? How would she feel if she was given a task to do that she wouldn't be able to complete because she didn't have the necessary digits or dexterity to do so? And what about when she gets to that age when appearance is everything to a girl? How will she feel when her teenage friends are wearing rings and imitating those crap party dances on MTV? How would she deal with it all?

I concluded that it probably wouldn't be a problem for her at all when she was young. Indeed, I reckoned other children wouldn't even look twice at her hand until she got to at least primary school age. Of course, things would change when she got to about 5, 6 or 7 as this is when kids generally become aware of the differences amongst their peers. Surely being teased would make her self-conscious; make her withdrawn – wouldn't it?

I thought that this situation would probably be a little easier to deal with if we were having a boy. After all, he could at least make a decent fist with his good hand! It made me angry and sad at the same time. Knowing that other people – even if they were just young kids – would deliberately upset my little girl made me want to just give her a big cuddle right there and then. I really did just want to have her with me then so I could hug her and tell her everything would be OK.

And then I got around to wondering how Sally and I would deal with it? How would we be able to stop ourselves from over-compensating; being over-protective? Should we even try to stop ourselves? Would *we* feel self-conscious? The last thing I remember thinking before I eventually fell asleep was that I wished – more than anything – that the scan with the consultant would come round very quickly.

After I woke the next day, I got straight on the computer and started researching the topic of fingerless hands in greater detail. After a while, I noticed one word popping up more and more often - 'symbrachydactyly'.

Wikipedia describes symbrachydactyly as: "... *A congenital abnormality, characterized by limb anomalies consisting of brachydactyly, cutaneous syndactyly and global hypoplasia of the hand or, rarely, foot. In many cases, bones will be missing from the fingers and some fingers may be missing altogether.*"

It also went on to say that:

"The cause of symbrachydactyly is unknown. One possible cause might be an interruption of the blood supply to the developing arm at four to six weeks of pregnancy. There is no link to anything the mother did or did not do during pregnancy."

This was consistent with the bleeding that Sal experienced when we feared she was about to have an ectopic pregnancy back in December. However, the best was left for last:

"In most cases, children born with symbrachydactyly are able to adapt to their physical limitations and experience a fully functional life with no treatment. Possible treatment includes surgery or a routine of regularly stretching the fingers."

Treatment?

For the first time in what seemed like an age, I felt a pang of positivity run through me. I spent the next hour or so looking through a plethora of articles and information about possible treatments for symbrachydactyly. In fact, there were a number of things that could be done, procedures that could help to ensure my little girl was at the very least, less disadvantaged. These procedures ranged from grafting toes onto the hand, to extending existing fingers over a period of time with a specialist device. Moreover, there were also prosthetics available which could help to give an afflicted hand a more normal appearance.

There were options. I suddenly felt quite optimistic; quite happy even. Armed with this, I called Sally away from her half-term slumber in front of *This Morning* to join me in the spare room.

She liked what she saw and was particularly impressed by a newspaper article I had shown her, entitled *Hope For Children Born Without Fingers*. This well-written piece described (in somewhat painful detail it must be said) a 'stretching' treatment which has been pioneered by doctors at the Great Ormond Street Hospital in London. After reading this twice, Sally turned to me and said 'That's exactly what I needed to see.'

There were options.

Over the next few days, Sally and I did our best to 'get on with getting on'. We had more or less come to terms with the idea our little girl would enter the world with a 'disadvantaged' hand; however, the fact that there were things which could be done seemed to mitigate the darker thoughts we had initially been besieged by.

And so we kept ourselves busy. I worked every day and found solace in writing bland articles and blogs about fountain pens, HGV driver training courses and drug rehabilitation clinics. Sally cleaned the bungalow from top to bottom and found things to do out and about with Clare and Finley. Although we felt better than we had on Tuesday it is fair to say we really couldn't wait for the next scan appointment to come round.

To me, the scan with the consultant could go one of two ways. The best case scenario was that it would reveal Laura had made an error at the initial scan and that in actual fact the fingers had been there all along.

Unlikely; but possible.

The other scenario was that the second scan would confirm the findings of the first and tell us that our child – more likely than not – had symbrachydactyly.

This is what I was expecting.

Sally on the other hand, had a third scenario – a worst case scenario. She had conducted her own research and had found that anomalies with hands can – in some cases - be evidence of anomalous chromosome-based conditions like Trisomy 18. Her greatest fear was that the forthcoming scan would reveal our baby girl had significantly more wrong with her than a few missing fingers. In fact, she said that she now viewed symbrachydactyly as being 'almost a good thing'.

Although I tried to reassure Sal that nothing I had read about and nothing we had been told by Laura supported this; I couldn't rule out the possibility of something more convoluted being wrong. After all, I'm not an impartial, professionally trained doctor – I'm just someone who wants my little girl to be happy and healthy. Sally confided in me that the thought of having a child with something like Trisomy 18 terrified her. She asked me what my thoughts were; what I thought we should do if the consultant turned round and presented us with this worst case scenario. I thought about it for a while and then I hugged her close to me.

'Whatever happens', I said, 'We'll deal with it.'

5

Sally and I arrived at the hospital 45 minutes early for our follow-up scan with the consultant. The last few days of limbo had been somewhat tortuous so we wanted to get things rolling – in any direction – as quickly as we possibly could.

After waiting in the busy main waiting room of the Mother & Child Department for what seemed like an age, we were finally called and taken through to a part of the building we hadn't visited before by a middle-aged man in scrubs who turned out to be Martin, our consultant. Martin was an articulate yet softly-spoken man whose whole persona exuded experience and expertise. Although I felt nervous, I found his presence quite reassuring. Soon enough, we were taken into an examination room which had all the usual ultrasound equipment, minus the ceiling-hung monitor. Sally and I both assumed our respective positions as Martin read through our notes and re-iterated to us why we had been asked to come back for a second scan.

Once we were all ready, the gel went on, the wand did its business and the images started appearing on the monitor on Martin's workstation.

Silence.

I could sense Sally's anxiety as she craned her neck to try and see what was appearing on the monitor. I too felt my stomach double-over as I scanned the fuzzy image for evidence of digits.

Still Martin said nothing.

I looked at Sal but she was too focused on the monitor to notice. Martin eventually started to speak:

'OK. So here we have the spine; down there are the feet; that there is the heartbeat...'

'Yes, yes, yes' I thought – 'the fingers, man; show us the fucking fingers!!'

'Ah. Your little girl has decided to lie right next to the wall of the uterus so it is difficult to see exactly what is happening with the left hand.'

Sal and I were leaning over now, practically willing the monitor to give up its secrets. And then I saw it. And so did Michael.

'Well; Laura was right to flag this up. She really is one of the very best we have you know'

I felt my hopes of any kind of initial error drain away and looked over at Sal to see what her reaction was. She was still completely focused on the monitor.

'From what I can see, it appears there is a thumb and three digits; however, these have not developed to the same length which the fingers on the right hand have...'

He gestured to the monitor and highlighted where our little girl was using the fingers on her right hand to cover her face. '..And therefore they are likely to be significantly shorter than you would expect them to be at birth. 'Three fingers', I said 'She definitely has three fingers?'

For some reason, I felt buoyed by this news. After all, three fingers – short or otherwise - were three fingers more than she had this time last week.

'Three digits', Michael corrected, 'and a thumb.'

The disappointment I had felt earlier at not hearing the words "It's all been a big mistake on Laura's part" seemed to evaporate. Surely having three fingers, digits, stumps, nubbins or whatever they were was better than having nothing there at all. Surely it would provide her with greater functionality. Surely it would improve her chances of being able to benefit from surgical treatments or prosthetics later on in life.

We threw all of these questions, as well as many more, at Martin. He told us that this was, regrettably, not his field of expertise and therefore he didn't feel qualified to give us definite (or even half definite) answers to queries of such a sensitive nature. However, he acknowledged that we should get answers to our questions as quickly as possible as this would enable us to be better prepared for whatever might lay ahead. And so he said, if we would care to wait outside for five or ten minutes, he would make a few phone calls to some of the research hospitals in our region and see if they could get one of their specialists to see us.

After waiting ten short minutes in the main foyer, Martin came out and handed Sally her dossier.

'I've made an appointment for you to see a specialist at the Department of Fetal Medicine over at Addenbrokes Hospital in Cambridge on Thursday evening.'

An appointment with a specialist at one of the top hospitals in the country in two days. Outstanding.

'I've also written up your notes and sent a letter and email to your GP'.

I was hugely impressed by Martin. He was a man who got things done without any fanfare or fuss. The NHS is full of incredibly efficient and modest individuals like him and I think people would do well to remember this when they moan about the service's shortcomings.

'We really appreciate what you've done', I said as I reached out to shake his hand.

'Think nothing of it', he said. 'Good luck'.

Sal and talked in terms which were far more upbeat than they had been during the previous week. Whilst Sally was still concerned about larger chromosome-based anomalies, she agreed that things now seemed far more promising than they had. Although this scan could hardly be construed as 'good news', I felt a lot more positive now I knew we were actually moving forward.

I slept a lot better that night. And the next too.

6

Cambridge is little more than an hour's drive away from where we live so getting to where we needed to be was straightforward enough. Again, we arrived stupidly early for our appointment so we took the opportunity to have a look around the hospital.

Addenbrookes is a huge hospital which is made up of a plethora of individual hospitals, clinics, research facilities and countless other buildings. It's like Heathrow Airport – it's grown so big that it now has its own shopping centre, food court, Barclays Bank and on-site solicitors (could catch on I think).

After a great deal of aimless walking, the time finally came for us to make our way to the Fetal Medicine Department. We were still twenty minutes early and so we settled down in the department's thoroughly contemporary yet completely empty waiting room to experience that 'time slowing down' sensation that medical facilities seem to engender so well.

However, this was not to be as we were invited to 'come through' by a nurse a good fifteen minutes ahead of our allotted time. This had to be a good sign. We were lead into a darkened suite where two men were waiting for us, one standing next to a bed with monitors above and adjacent to it in the middle of the room, the other sat with his back to us looking at a bank of three large monitors that looked to me like a flight simulator. The seated man span round and introduced himself as James, the specialist consultant. The gentleman at the side of the bed was Hassan, a senior clinical fellow.

It was clear that Sal and I were now enjoying a level of medical care that was a step-up from the norm. The monitors above the bed had separate feeds which displayed both ultrasound and 3D images while the bank of monitors flashed up graphs and pictures which looked like they were engineering a small foreign war. I was very impressed; not just by the high-tech nature of it all, but by the fact we had been given access to it within 72 hours and hadn't had to pay a penny for the privilege.

After making herself comfortable on the bed and being dolloped with an almost comical amount of lubricant, Sally focused her attention immediately on the monitor hanging from the ceiling right in front of her. I sat on the chair next to the bed and flicked my observations between the same screen and the monitor that was on Hassan's workstation at the other side of the bed.

And so we got underway.

Hassan narrated us through the crystal clear images that were coming through on the screens – James, now sitting in his chair at the end of the bed, remained silent as he looked dispassionately at the workstation monitor. I glanced up at Sally. She seemed to be quite at ease. She really is a trooper. When I looked back at the screen I saw a hand. 'The problem was with the left hand?' James asked, seemingly to no-one in particular.

'Yes' we replied.

He must have seen something that I'd missed as he immediately asked Hassan to zoom in and 'pull it up'. Within moments, Hassan had activated a button and then a dial which enabled him to effectively trap the image and then look at it from any angle he liked.

Now I was really impressed. James leaned forward and examined the image closer.

'Well', he said in hushed yet purposeful tones, 'it looks as though there is a standard looking thumb and forefinger, as well as three fingers which appear to be undeveloped past the proximal phlange'.

I looked at the screen but couldn't translate what he had said into an image I could recognise.

'So she's got four fingers?', I said.

'Yes, look here.' James pointed at the workstation screen even though it was more than a metre away from him. 'You can see that there is a fully formed thumb, a seemingly fully formed forefinger, and then three fingers which are missing two thirds of their constituent parts.'

I looked harder but still struggled to put it all together.

James createde a shape with his hand that was very similar to the one little boys make when they are pretending to shoot a gun; namely an extended thumb and forefinger and three fingers bent over into the palm. He then reversed this so that I could see it only from the 'outside'. It looked like he was 'giving me the bird', but with his forefinger instead of the more offensive middle one.

'This is how her hand is.'

Like the scan two days ago, I had been given what was effectively bad news. At that particular moment however it seemed like anything but. I looked at Sal and held her gaze as I replied to James.

'So she could – in theory - tie her own laces, cut up her own food, ride a bike...' I trailed off, smiling at Sal.

'Yes, she could conceivably do a great many things if the area is functional', James replied. 'Certainly, having a working thumb and forefinger', he made a pincer type motion with his hand, 'really is very beneficial as it can be used for all manner of everyday tasks.'

A massive wave of positivity gushed through my veins. Not only did she have the right number of fingers, she also – potentially - had the ability to do things: lots of things.

I beamed a smile and told James and Hassan that we had spent most of the last week thinking our little girl would be born with no fingers whatsoever. Now we had learnt she had four digits, one of which was completely as it should be, we felt like we had won the lottery. James seemed pleased for us but felt compelled to inject a bit of caution into proceedings.

'It must be said that...', he looked at Sal then me, '...there is no way of knowing whether the thumb or forefinger will be fully functional so that is something that you must bear in mind'. I held his look.

'We've not actually seen any movement from the digits on the left hand during this scan so there is no way we can say for certain that the hand will be fully functional.'

'Yes', I said, feeling suitably chastised. Hassan took this moment to interject: 'From what we have seen however, it looks as though the bones of the left arm have developed quite normally, and this is often a good indicator that the associated muscles are likely to be in good shape.'

On hearing this, I made a gesture to suggest I was about to reply with another question but, for some reason, my mind went entirely blank. I looked at Hassan's monitor and just seemed to experience a very brief involuntary daydream of some kind. It was very strange.

Sal took this as her cue to take up the Q & A baton. 'Do you know what may have caused this to happen?', she said.

James leaned back in his chair and gave us both an all-knowing look.

'What have you been looking at on the Internet?' he quickly replied.

Well, I have been worried that it may have something to do with a chromosome disorder – y'know the whole clenched fist thing; while Ferrel has been thinking it is...' she then looked over at me: '...what was that thing you were looking into?'

Suddenly I was back in the room. 'Symbrachydactyly' I said, hoping I had pronounced it properly. And this is where James really earned his money.

In a very long and comprehensive reply, James explained to us what he thought the cause of the problem was. He told us in great detail that, although he couldn't disregard it completely, it was unlikely to be symbrachydactyly as this was - amongst other things - more related to 'claw hand'-type conditions. It was also unlikely to be anything related to chromosome abnormalities as there were no 'markers' (such as clenched fists) to support this. Moreover, he told us that the fact our baby's hand problem was asymmetrical, i.e. it wasn't evident in the right hand or left foot, also meant that this was more than likely an isolated event.

An isolated event which he believed was almost certainly caused by an amniotic band injury.

From what I could gather, amniotic bands are strands of amniotic membrane which can get tangled up with any part of a foetus in the early stages of pregnancy. James' theory was that some of these bands had wrapped themselves around three fingers on our little girl's left hand, effectively stopping them from developing. I looked over at Sal as James was summing up. I could almost see the two metaphorical anvils that had made her shoulders their home for the past week disappear as a slightly reluctant half-smile broke across her face, along with an extended exhalation of breath.

'That really was exactly what I wanted to hear', she said.

James finished his briefing by saying that, whilst this scan (and his subsequent assessment) was no guarantee of our child being born without anything more wrong with her than a few missing digits; he would consider our little girl to be no more at risk of having a significant problem at birth than any other newborn. Sal's face had the same look on it as it does whenever she watches that bit in *Dirty Dancing* when Patrick Swayze says something about putting a baby in a corner. She was very, very pleased indeed. And so was I.

As Sally wiped herself clean and the appointment drew to a close, James told us that he would book us an appointment with the hospital's Joint-Skeletal Clinic as this would provide us with the opportunity to find out more about the possible surgical and prosthetic options which are available these days. This was quite a surreal moment. Talking about possible surgical options for my unborn child would have seemed like the end of the world a fortnight ago. Standing in front of James' super-duper flight simulator at that moment however, I felt more positive and optimistic than I had done for ages.

Happiness is relative and I was certainly relatively happy at that point.

Our time with James and Hassan had been incredibly beneficial and we thanked them profusely when the time came to say goodbye. I am not the kind of person who normally gushes about people who simply do the job they are trained and paid to do; in this case however, I really did want to express my gratitude for helping us to get a greater grip on what had been a very testing time for the two of us. They were very matter of fact about their roles and wished us the very best of luck.

Swift, excellent care given by superb healthcare professionals absolutely free of charge. Surely the NHS is the single greatest socialist endeavour there has ever been.

As we left the Department of Fetal Medicine, Sally and I walked back through the labyrinthine corridors with far more purpose, taking it in turns to repeat the largely positive things we had just been told. We did this all the way back to the car, as well as for most of the drive home. Although we didn't really have the right to, we felt – for want of a better word - elated. We concluded that, as long as the hand turned out to be functional, our little girl would get along just fine.

When we finally got exhausted of repeating James' briefing, we had a little moment of silence. Unlike the moments of silence we had shared over the past week or so though, this one didn't have an overwhelming air of melancholy hanging over it. Sally eventually broke the silence:

'I can actually enjoy being pregnant now', she said. 'I can get on with things like buying baby clothes and sorting out the bits we have been given for Bump.'

'Yes', I said, patting her thigh. 'Yes you can'.

7

It seems odd to think I felt like my world had caved in two weeks ago.

To all extents and purposes, things have gone back to being 'as you were' since we came back from our appointment with James and Hassan at Addenbrookes. Now that Sal and I know more or less where we stand with our baby's hand, a lot of the fear, the apprehension, and many of the other negative thoughts that hung over us day and night seem to have dissipated. Sure, our little girl will have issues with her hand. But, if a somewhat limited grip and some vague aesthetic concerns are the full extent of the problem, that is not so bad really. Indeed, our thinking now is that - in the grand scheme of things - a few missing digits is by no means the worst thing that a new born baby could be saddled with.

And I can't tell you how much better this new way of thinking makes us both feel.
Like I said, things feel very much like they are returning to normal. Sally is back at work after the Easter break, my Mum is back to rambling on about the weather whenever she phones and I'm relaxed enough to sit and play my football game on the PlayStation for a few hours rather than go walking round the block at all hours of the day or night. It's not like we're ignoring the fact our baby will be a little bit different when she is born; it's just that we now know roughly what to expect; therefore we feel comfortable enough to remove it – at least for a few hours of the day – from the very front of our minds (until our next appointment at Addenbrookes comes round, anyway).

This new wave of – I'm hesitant to call it optimism, but I will – has had a really positive effect on Sal. No longer tormenting herself with the possibility of chromosome-based disorders, Sally has enjoyed being pregnant more over the past few days than she has at any other time since before Christmas. She has been ironing the baby clothes my Mum bought us, sorting through all of the bits and bobs we have been given, and started looking through brochures from the likes of Mothercare, Boots and the Early Learning Centre.

And it really is lovely to see.

Sal has not had anything like an easy ride over the past few months, what with the ectopic pregnancy scare, her persistent fatigue, multiple bouts of illness and of course the stress and worry of dealing with what's gone on over the last couple of weeks. Although I have been here to help in any way I can, it is Sal who has had to 'feel' all of the effects which this adversity has thrown at her – not me. She is the one who has had to carry a fledgling life within her and deal with all the fear, ailments and even perceived guilt which that entails.

And she has dealt with it all marvellously.
Sure she was a bit mardy a month or so ago but show me a pregnant woman who doesn't get moody and I'll show you an episode of *Eastenders* where nobody shouts.

The point is, Sally has had to deal with an inordinate amount of stress and anxiety over the past few months. To be sure, I think most other people would have simply fallen to bits if they were faced with what she has had to put up with and I must say I am incredibly proud of the way she has handled it.

You wouldn't think it to look at her - all sugar and spice and all things nice - but she really is a trooper. She's made of the right stuff alright and it is testament to her that she can pick herself up and carry on regardless after getting knocked down so many times.

To say I admire her for that is perhaps the understatement of the century.

If our little girl is fortunate enough to inherit Sally's fortitude – as well as my stoic stubbornness – I have absolutely no doubt she will overcome anything and everything that dares to stand in her way.

8

I remember reading somewhere many years ago that the arrival of a child can help to bring parents-to-be and would-be grandparents closer together.

I am hoping very much that this is true.

It would be fair to say that my parents and I have enjoyed a very up-and-down relationship over the course of my 38 years on this planet. When I was a young child, I absolutely adored my Mum and Dad. To me they were everything that parents should be. My Mum was always keen to spend time with me and liked nothing more than giving me lots of fuss and hugs. My Dad was far less tactile yet was very enthusiastic when it came to sharing his passion for things like cars and trains. As an only child, I got plenty of love, plenty of attention and perhaps most importantly - plenty of presents at Christmas time.

When my Dad was employed, he worked mainly as a van driver, taking bits and pieces from firms across North London to destinations all over the country. Some of my earliest memories are of the three of us throwing a mattress in the back of his van and spontaneously taking off for an overnight jaunt or long weekend to one of the places he would be going – just for the hell of it.

I loved it.

When my dad wasn't working, my Mum would often try and help make ends meet by cleaning offices in the evenings. Whilst tidying up commercial buildings wasn't quite as exciting as racing off to Blackpool on a whim, I still remember enjoying it as my Mum would find me some paper from somewhere and let me doodle while she vacuumed the workplaces of people who earned far more money than we would ever see.

We weren't well off by any stretch of the imagination but that didn't seem to matter too much (aside from when all my friends got Commodore 64s one Christmas and I got a Commodore 16 because that's all my Mum & Dad could afford - it mattered plenty then!). But what I didn't receive in early personal computing power was more than made up for by what I gained from my parents each and every day. They gave me unadulterated care and affection mixed in with a decent smattering of old-school discipline and tough love.

It was indeed a very happy childhood and memories of impossibly long summer holidays, 30-a-side football matches, pencil thin skateboards, mammoth games of cards at Christmas and ALWAYS playing outside no matter what the weather was doing brings a very broad and content smile to my face.

But then I became a teenager and everything changed.

To everyone's surprise, I developed into quite a bright teenager. This made me quite lazy (not to mention arrogant) at secondary school as I found I could complete most of the work I was given without having to really push myself too hard. Looking back now, I can see that being the parent of an able yet lazy, arrogant teenage boy must have been a massive chore. It must have driven my Dad absolutely nuts because I can remember it was at this point in my life that our relationship stuttered, stagnated and then very abruptly turned to absolute shit. For some reason, we just couldn't bear to be around one another at that time. When we did speak, we argued - about anything and everything. You name it; we fell out over it. It just seemed to me that, as soon as I became independent-minded, my dad felt the need to try and show me that he was – and always would be - the top man. Seriously, it didn't matter what I did or didn't do when I was 14, 15, and 16 – it was wrong.

Eventually – and inevitably - it got to the point where something had to give. So, when I was 17 I left home. I'd already stopped going to my A-level classes in Sixth Form anyway so I just thought 'Fuck it!' and left. A friend of mine in the year above me at school had decided to go and do a BTEC Sports Science course in Nottingham so I tagged along, rented a room in a sketchy council estate on the outskirts of the city and enrolled to do the same course as him at the same college (and I didn't have to pay for it because I was under 18 – result!).

Looking back now, it was the best thing that could have happened. I know my Mum wouldn't agree. In fact I think she holds a grudge with dad to this day for 'forcing' me out. But the truth is, moving away, making new friends and standing on my own two feet made me forget all about my problems with Dad. Instead of dealing with him every day, I was studying (very lazily it has to be said) something I had a genuine interest in and was, in the main, loving life.

I spent two great years in Nottingham. As well as making some good friends, staying in various different shared houses and obtaining a BTEC National Diploma in Sports Science; I attended – and passed - a 'Become a swimming pool lifeguard' course; quite unaware that it would lead me to take advantage of a whole plethora of future job opportunities and enable me to embrace a seasonal way of life that would become my bread and butter for the next decade.

But more important than all of that – moving away to Nottingham saved my relationship with my Dad. That may sound a little trite and melodramatic but it is actually quite true. Being away from his ever-watchful eye allowed me to look at things from a different perspective and even see him in a slightly more mature way.

Happily, the cold war between me and my Dad has continued to thaw nicely after that teenage Cuban Missile Crisis-type moment. Indeed, he has become quite unrecognisable to the unreasonable control freak he once was (although he is still as stubborn as oak at times). In fact, it is hard to believe that the man who is all giggles and smiles whenever he comes up to visit, and plays on the Wii with the enthusiasm of a small child, is the same man who once made my life quite unbearable.

I have no idea how the dynamic between us will alter once Bump comes into the world. I imagine he will actually have a good chuckle to himself when he sees me being forced to put up with the type of petulant behaviour he used to get from me! Maybe I will garner a deeper appreciation of what he had to deal with when I find myself saying things like 'As long as you live under my roof you'll live by my rules...!'

Perhaps the fact that becoming a parent lets you see things from the other side of the coin so-to-speak is what brings parents and children closer together when a grandchild joins the family.

There is a great quote from the original – and best – *Superman* film where Marlon Brando says something along the lines of: 'The son becomes the father and the father becomes the son'. Although it is slightly esoteric, I interpret this as being relative to the moment a son reaches the time of his life when he himself realises just what it is to undertake the responsibilities of fatherhood, like his father did before him. I also understand it to mean that this is the moment when the grandfather can take a step back and enjoy some of the benefits of his son's new found appetite for responsibility.

Of course, I could be wrong about the whole thing: it could just be some artsy-fartsy improvised dialogue that Brando came up with before spouting the drivel he got paid millions for on *Apocalypse Now*.

It doesn't matter though. I am very firmly of the opinion that having a child will make the three of us as close as we were when I was a kid. And that will be just lovely - for all of us.

9

It has now been roughly six months since Sally fell pregnant. Although not much mention of it is made in Sally's pregnancy books, the six month mark feels like quite a big deal to me. Perhaps because of this, I have spent quite a bit of time this week thinking about how much things have changed since Sally first appeared by my bedside five or so months ago waving her 'novelty pen' at me with a massive grin on her face. Six months ago, I found it hard to believe that I would ever actually become a dad. Indeed, I was seriously considering whether or not Sal would be better off being with someone else instead of me; someone who would be able to give her the child she so dearly wanted. Six months ago, Sally and I were having sex on a near daily basis. In fact, she was literally harassing me in to bed every time I came in the door. Six months ago, Finley was just about as far gone as our little bump is now.

Now; I have fully realised the fact that I am definitely going to be a dad (all being well) and I'm not conceiving any plans for Sal to hate me enough to run off with another man (not consciously anyway). Moreover, I am getting about as much sex as the International Space Station's caretaker and Finley is about the same size as Orville the Duck (he's a proper little chubber now).

All within six months. Amazing.

Of course, reaching a landmark event doesn't just make you look back; it makes you look forward as well. Although I know it's going to happen, it seems incredible to think that the baby inside Sal's belly – our little girl - will actually be here in three month's time. It must be true because we have all the clothes, toys, towels and blankets ready to accommodate her as soon as she arrives. But for some reason, inside my head at least, it just doesn't seem like it's going to happen.

I don't say that because I have any concerns about the pregnancy failing; I say it because the concept of seeing

Sal's belly bulge pop and produce a brand new human being just seems so surreal that I don't think my brain can process it.

I think the truth of the matter is that I have got quite used to Sal being a pregnant woman. I have got used to the monopolisation of the sofa, the abstention from wine and the frequent trips to the toilet. I have got used to the constant browsing online for buggies, posing in front of the mirror with a frown, and a fanatical need to have every DIY task ever conceived finished before August.

I am in the eye of the storm - I no longer regard Sally's pregnancy as being a process with a definite beginning and end; I just see it as being 'the norm'.

Of course, there are plenty of things telling me that the finish line is closer than I may think. For instance, Sally's pregnancy books tell me that our little girl is now, to all intents and purposes, fully formed, i.e. how she is now is how she will be when she arrives in August. Furthermore, I even felt her kick when I rested my hand on Sally's belly the other day. If she's kicking then she must be restless; and if she's restless then she must be looking for ways to escape.

She's coming. And sooner rather than later. But still my brain doesn't seem able to register it.

It's bizarre really because I can't wait for her to be here, I really can't. Truly, the thought of finally holding our little one in my arms makes me feel all soft and soppy inside.
So really, not being able to process the idea of her actually arriving in the real world sometime in mid-August doesn't make any sense at all.

But then maybe it isn't supposed to.

Maybe this is just one of those unique moments in life that the human mind is unable to fully comprehend After all, I have never had a child before so my brain doesn't have any experience to draw upon. Moreover, I cannot experience the intrinsic intimacy that Sal feels so I don't have any kind of hormonal gauges to call on either. I am as a man perhaps just pre-programmed to 'go with the flow' and take the pregnancy process one day at a time. And that suits me just fine.

Now that I have managed to put my concerns about Bump's left hand a little further toward the background of my consciousness (for the time being at least), I have found this stage of the pregnancy to be – quite surprisingly - the most enjoyable. I have enjoyed seeing my Mum and Dad getting excited whenever they come up to visit and see Sal's belly looking larger than the time before. I have enjoyed watching Sally getting all clucky and soppy when she gets new baby clothes to add to the Imelda Marcos-type collection which has taken over the recently completed walk-in cupboard in the spare room/home office/nursery. I have enjoyed humming *Waterloo Sunset* over and over again next to Sally's belly so that our little girl will have an innate appreciation of good music when she does finally decide to put in an appearance.

I have enjoyed doing all of these things, as well as many others besides, so I really don't mind taking each day one at a time when things are like this.

Of course, things will move on. Six months will become seven, then eight, and then nine. And, whilst I really cannot wait for mid-August to come 'round, it does feel nice to finally be at a stage where Sally and I both genuinely seem to be enjoying this once in a lifetime experience.

10

Whilst it is fair to say I always wanted Bump to be a boy, I have come to the conclusion that there are a number of advantages to having a daughter.

I have noticed a number of things recently which have lead me to believe this.

For example, when I went for my daily walk around the park earlier on today, I saw a group of girls and a group of boys, none of them older than ten or eleven, milling around the ramps and moguls on the BMX track. The girls were sat atop one of the larger ramps, chatting away to each other at a decibel level which could hardly be heard. The boys on the other hand, were bouncing around the track like demented kangaroos and screaming all kinds of nonsense at the top of their voices.

It is surely just a fact that boys are genetically wired to behave like little bell-ends a good 75 per cent of the time.

In fact, it seems obvious to me that the male half of

Britain's population, from the moment they start school until nine months before they are due to become fathers, are conditioned by nature to be as irritating as they can possibly be.

This behaviour is often explained away as 'boys being boys', i.e. little toe-rags living up to the relatively low expectations society has of them. Of course, this is not true of all boys, nor is it true of most boys all of the time. What is true however is that boys, by in large, are significantly more 'difficult' to deal with than girls.

Obviously, girls can be troublesome too. I am under no illusion that little girls (and indeed big girls) can be every bit as nauseating and irritating as the worst behaved boys. However, the thing with girls is that being out of order is often the exception rather than the rule for them. For boys it's far too often the other way round.

And this leads me neatly onto another advantage of having a girl – they don't fight (at least they don't in this nice little middle-class enclave we currently live in). Physical aggression is something which most boys inevitably have to deal with when they're growing up. Whether it's a little bit of play fighting in the school playground, an angry scrap on the football pitch or an encounter with some 'youths' in a quiet alleyway; boys will invariably find themselves up against it at some point in their lives.

There can be times when physical confrontation can be an effective form of tough love as it can teach a growing lad that adversity and conflict are unwelcome yet inescapable parts of life. However, it is fair to say that - in a world where knives are now all too common – no father in their right mind would choose to put their son in harm's way just so that they can learn a life lesson.

Thankfully, this is something that doesn't apply to girls so much. Aside from the androgynous female-gangs that hang around our inner cities like packs of hyenas, girls don't really have to worry too much about being set upon by other girls as the female mentality doesn't regard physical supremacy as being overly important (although this clearly does not apply to most provincial UK towns on Friday/Saturday nights).

Naturally I, as the father-to-be of a little girl who will at best only be able to make one decent fist in any event, am pleased that this is the case. After all, having a little girl should mean that I:

1. Won't need to watch my child come home from school with a black eye or broken nose, and;
2. Won't need to beat up another child's father in order to prove violence solves nothing.

There was one other thing I saw this week which made me think there are advantages to having a daughter. What I saw was very simple, very lovely and very profound - it was a young teenage girl walking arm-in-arm with her father along the high street.

This got me thinking that - as long as I don't manage to somehow make her hate me - my daughter will more than likely be quite happy to show her affection for me all throughout her life. Girls don't seem to go through that stage where they emotionally distance themselves from their fathers in the way that young men do; therefore I can (hopefully) expect my little girl to hold my hand, give me hugs, and walk arm-in-arm with me until I shuffle off this mortal coil. I like that thought. I really, really do. It makes me feel kind of immortal somehow.

Naturally, I can appreciate that there are also a number of

'disadvantages' to having a daughter. From a father's point of view, surely the worst thing about having a daughter must be the fear of her being assaulted by a man. Whilst getting beaten up is a bad thing to happen to a boy, it is arguably the worst thing that can happen to them.

Getting beaten up is not the worst thing that can happen to a girl.

Even though my little girl is now safely tucked away in her Mum's belly and will not have an inkling of the kind of malice that some men are capable of for many years; I know for a fact that I will worry about her safety for the rest of my life.

But as the old knight at the end of *Indiana Jones and the Last Crusade* wisely remarked:

"This is the price of immortality".

THE THIRD TRIMESTER

1

Yes, we're now into the final push (no pun intended); the final hurrah if you like. In around twelve weeks time, Sally and I will no longer be just a couple; we will be parents to our very own baby girl and co-founders of our own little family.

Incredible.

Sally and I got a taste of things to come today as Clare and John left Finley in our care while they took a day off to go stock hunting for their fledgling online cosmetics business.

On the whole, it was actually quite a pleasant experience as, aside from a brief spell where he got a little bit grizzly, he was pretty chilled-out all day.

To get our family day off to a pleasant, Disney-like start I thought it would be a nice idea to treat the little man to a few tunes on my guitar. I wasn't overly optimistic of the outcome of this as my guitar – much like my ability to play it – isn't very impressive. Nevertheless, I sat him down in his little vibrating chair in the living room and positioned myself on the floor next to him so that he could see and hear the strings being played. He looked curiously at me as I sat down and seemed a little bit intimidated as I rested the guitar on my lap. The look on his face quickly flicked between wonder, incredulity, fear and hilarity as I gently endeavoured to do 'House of the Rising Sun' a modicum of justice. His feet were wiggling and his arms were, for want of a better word, 'fitting' but I didn't get the feeling he was really enjoying what he was hearing.

After concluding that the chubby young music aficionado in front of me was not a big fan of the finger-plucking variety of guitar music, I instead opted to treat him to a little bit of chord play. So I strummed a gentle progression through some minor chords and looked to see if his face had a more impressed look on it.

It didn't.

His feet were still moving and his arms were going like the clappers but he didn't look very happy. In fact, he looked like he had soiled himself so I duly leaned over and gave him a quick smell check just to make sure that wasn't the case.

Happily, it wasn't.

Already half way through my entire back catalogue and I was struggling. Next I gave him the *James Bond* theme. Nothing. After that, some 12-bar blues. That got a burp. I even tried the melody that runs all the way through REM's *Everybody Hurts* in the hope that it might sound a bit like a lullaby but all I got in return was the same fractured sequence of wonder, incredulity, fear and hilarity as before. It was clear to me - I needed a new guitar.

After conceding defeat with the musical approach, we decided that it would be a good idea to make the most of the blue skies and bright sunshine and take Finley out somewhere where there was plenty of fresh air to breathe and interesting things to see.

Fortunately, we only live about ten miles away from a large stately home that is surrounded by gloriously verdant grounds where hundreds of deer roam free. Perfect we thought – animals and fresh air – let's go.

But that's not how it works with a small child, is it?

Oh no, you can't just decide to go somewhere, get in the car and leave. Apparently, you have to do a double-check of everything you'll ever, ever need and then pack and repack a bag that is about the size of Sherpa's rucksack. I think it's some kind of law.

After about ten minutes of getting Finley's 'essentials' sorted, we eventually made it out to the car. He was already in his car seat so all we needed to do was fasten that onto the back seat with one of the rear seatbelts. How hard could it be?

Well, whilst we found it easy enough to work out where the seat belt attached to Finley's seat, we just didn't seem to have enough belt left over at the end to snap the buckle into the safety clip. No matter how hard Sally and I pulled it, it was just a teensy, tiny little bit too short to snap in.

I felt like 'Doc' Emmet Brown when he was trying to plug in that electric cable on top of the clock tower in *Back to the Future.*

This didn't seem to bother Finley too much though as he was treating himself to a nice little mid-morning nap. After what seemed like an absolute age, we eventually re-routed the seat belt and got it to clip in safely. Apparently, this is much easier when you have the base of a child's car seat already positioned in the car. 'So where's the base?' I asked Sal.

'In Clare's car', she replied.

Unfortunately, the *Krypton Factor*-type challenges didn't end there. After a pleasant drive to the nearby stately home, we parked up and immediately set about attaching Finley's car seat to the accompanying buggy unit so that we could push him around. The buggy unit was a collapsible affair which snapped into place straight away and neatly accommodated the car seat on the top by way of two simple housings on the sides.

Once we had snapped the wheels on (which had pretty solid, heavy–duty tyres on them), the buggy was ready for business. I had to admit, it looked pretty good. Always thinking ahead mind, I asked Sal if it was just as easy to put away as it was to assemble. I thought this was a sensible question as we might well be tired after walking around in the sunshine and Finley may be awake by then.

Sally admitted that she didn't know how easy it was to pack away so we decided to have a go at it there and then.

Evidently, it is quite an easy buggy to pack away – if you're a fucking Charlie Babbit-type savant with a genius-like ability to apply advanced mechanical engineering and quantum theory mathematics to any given task. Needless to say, we pushed and pulled on the various different limbs of the buggy and depressed the randomly spaced buttons in all manner of different sequences but the bastard thing simply would not collapse. And all the while Finley stayed fast asleep.

As if by fate, Clare chose this very moment to call Sally's mobile. After a few pleasantries, Sally relayed her sister's instructions to me: 'There are two separate, grey coloured buttons on each 'leg' which are set at the same level but look nothing like each other. Push one of them forward while pushing the other one backwards.'

The buggy folded away into a neat pack. I shut my eyes, bit my lip and looked at Sally's phone with a degree of menace befitting someone who is criminally insane.

'All done!'

Ten minutes later and Sal and I were pushing a still sleeping Finley around the beautifully manicured grounds, soaking up the sunshine, enjoying the slightly rarefied ambience and keeping an eye out for deer. As well as plenty of foreign tourists, there were lots of parents strolling around the estate doing much the same thing with their young children.

I felt like I was being initiated into some kind of club.

Indeed, it got me to thinking: this is how I would be spending my weekends from now on. Saturdays and Sundays would not be about nights out on the ale or lying in bed with hangovers (not that they are now, really); no, my weekends would be made up of hours spent strolling around lakes, playing in parks, petting animals at farms and making sandcastles on beaches. But I didn't feel any kind of resentment about it. In fact, the prospect of doing these kinds of things didn't fill me with the kind of dread that I always feared they sub-consciously would; it just made me feel quite warm inside.

Yeah - I was ready to join this club.

Unfortunately, we didn't get to see any deer. Not that it mattered anyway because Finley slept the whole time we were there. Sally and I enjoyed it anyway though, walking around the estate like a proper mum and dad, being all grown up and respectable.

And the buggy was easy to put away when we got back to the car too.

2

I have spent the last few days pondering our upcoming appointment at Addenbrookes Hospital next week.

As well as (hopefully) revealing evidence of whether or not our little girl's left hand has any function, this appointment will tell us more about the things which can be done, both in terms of surgery and prosthetics, to improve Bump's outlook if need be. Oddly enough, neither Sal nor I seem too worried about this appointment. This may be because we're both feeling quite upbeat at the moment, or it may be because we sub-consciously believe that the news will not be bad (on account of our last appointment being so positive).

I really will be pretty broken up if it does turn out that Bump's little hand is incapable of functioning as it will limit her in so many ways. The daydreams that I continue to have of her, making daisy chains in the garden with Sal; finger plucking a child's guitar as I play mine, will simply not become anything other than dreams if her hand is unable to function at any level.

But as I said before, Sal and I both feel convinced that this will not be the case. We have scrutinised all of our previous ultrasound scan images and seen what we believe to be evidence of digits on her left hand appearing in different places on different pictures, thereby giving us all the reassurance we need to approach this next appointment with a relatively high degree of optimism.

Of course, we may just be fooling ourselves and setting ourselves up for a fall. I hope not. I really do hope not.

All I know is, if we return from Addenbrookes knowing our little girl's hand is the right size and has full function - albeit with three fewer digits than is fashionable - then Sal and I will be very happy bunnies indeed.

So I guess the only thing to do is wait and see what happens.

3

It has been yet another eventful week.

Unfortunately, our trip to Addenbrookes on Wednesday didn't reveal any more evidence of what our little girl's hand will or will not be capable of. I remember James (the consultant) telling us at the last appointment that seeing detailed images becomes harder as time goes by with a pregnancy and that was very much the case this time around.

James wasn't present for this appointment so it was left to Hassan to do the honours. As self-styled veterans of ultrasound scans, Sally and I took our respective positions without needing to be prompted. Hassan applied the gel, the room went silent and off we went again.

The first thing Hassan identified was the baby's heartbeat. Good. Next.

After this, he did the usual point-and-click stuff to measure growth and development. Fine. Next.

Gone were the days when seeing my child's heartbeat and facial features on a screen made me feel soppy.

The hand, man! Get to the hand!

After Hassan relayed the measurements to the nurse over by the flight simulator screens, the room went quiet again.

The silence persisted, punctuated only by Hassan making the odd sigh and taking in prolonged intakes of air. Despite his very cool and measured demeanour, it was clear that Hassan was getting just a little bit frustrated. Every now and then he would save an image on his console and work his magic to turn it into a 3D picture. Aside from a great shot of Bump's foot though, there really didn't seem to be much in the offing. Bump was being very uncooperative in the way she had decided to position herself and therefore Hassan simply didn't get many opportunities to see much of her left hand. In fact, the only half-decent image we saw at all was when he asked Sally to lie on her side so that he could use his ultrasound wand to get a view of Bump's forearms from over her shoulder.

(I felt a little bit sorry for Sal at this point as she is quite big now and I feared she might fall off the bed in a Del Trotter "play it cool, Trigger.." type way).
After a solid effort, Hassan inevitably conceded defeat and reiterated how difficult it can be to see details via ultrasound at this stage of a pregnancy. From what he did manage to see, he told us that Bump's measurements were all fine and that there didn't appear to be any significant changes (regarding her hand) from the last appointment. He also added that, while he couldn't be sure, he believed he saw the thumb of her left hand move at one point during the scan.

Movement equals function. Surely movement equals function.

After apologising for the lack of new information, Hassan invited Sally and I to go across the corridor and have a chat with Natalie, a specialist physiotherapy nurse from Addenbrookes Musco-Skeletal Department.

The room we went into looked like one of those rooms you see on TV medical documentaries where doctors take people to tell them bad news: all neutral colours and token soft furnishings. While Natalie had the manner of someone who was quite well versed in delivering difficult news, she didn't have to tell us anything we didn't already know. In fact, the bulk of our conversation consisted of her telling us how impressive modern prosthetics were and that some surgical options could be worth considering, depending on what was 'evidenced' at birth.

This was the long and the short of it. The scans could only

give us a rough idea as to how Bump's hand will turn out. It is not possible (or indeed wise) to make contingencies before the birth as there is no way of knowing exactly what the hand will look and function like until it can be physically observed and examined.

Whilst this made perfect sense, it made me feel like I was back in limbo a little bit. The semi-concrete answers I was hoping for hadn't materialised. There might be function; there might not. There might be a decent thumb and forefinger; there might not. What would be would be, etc.

I drifted off a bit as Natalie told us how there would be no need to come back to Addenbrokes and that everything else would hereon in be handled by our local hospital. Although I didn't feel disappointed per se, I felt the need to console myself by saying the same mantra in my head that I use to placate Sally whenever she starts to feel down about the situation:

'No matter how it turns out, there are things that can be done to make things better.'

After wrapping her conclusions up into a largely optimistic closing statement, Natalie took Sal and I to wait in the reception area while Hassan finished writing his report for Sally's ever-expanding dossier.

We took this opportunity to look through the reel of five image printouts which Hassan had handed to me as we left the ultrasound suite. There were two good 3D images of Bump's right hand, a great shot of her right foot and then the over-the-shoulder effort of her forearms. As we inspected this final image closer though, we became a little concerned by what we saw.

Although the image was poor in quality compared to the

others (perhaps because it was taken from a different viewpoint), it seemed to show the afflicted digits of the left hand poking out at differing angles in a slightly unnatural way. Moreover, the index finger which we had been led to believe was complete looked as though it was afflicted in much the same way as the other three digits. We looked at the picture from a variety of angles and put forward various theories as to why the fingers and digits appeared the way they did. Maybe the scan was incomplete before it was turned into a 3D image? Maybe Bump was using the hand to do a press-up on something that the scan didn't pick up on (thereby making her spread her digits).

After a short wait, the nurse turned up with Sally's file and we left to make our way back through The Pentagon-like corridors to the car park. Once we got to the car, Sally studied the picture again while I read the report:

'On the left hand, as previously noted, there is a thumb and index with three missing digits.'

There *is* an index finger.

'The findings today are consistent with the previous scan.'

I went over these things in my head as I shared them with Sal.

'Yes, but look': she showed me the unsettling image again. It doesn't look right; does it?'

It didn't.

The words on the page in front of me just didn't seem to marry up with the image we were both staring at. Rather than feeling like happy bunnies, Sally and I drove out of Addenbrookes car park feeling more than a little disconcerted. What we had heard and read told us that everything was pretty much as we expected it to be. In fact, there was even some evidence of movement and functionality. If anything we should have been feeling at least a little bit positive. But that picture. There was something about that picture.

This was our last scan. The next time we will see our little girl's left hand will be when she is using it to hold my thumb in the delivery room. In between now and then there will be no way of knowing whether the words in the report or the images from the scan are the best indicator of what our baby's hand will be like.

I turned and looked at Sal as we cruised home along the M11.

'Don't worry' I said, patting her belly gently.

'No matter how it turns out, there are things that can be done to make it better.'

She nodded, gave me a half-hearted smile and then didn't say another word until we got home.

4

All being well, I will be a dad in just under two months' time. Think of it, eight weeks from now there will be a whole new person in the world who will, to all intents and purposes, be a little version of me and Sal.

This has been going round my head for the last couple of days; not because I am beginning to sweat about Bump's impending arrival but because I am having trouble reconciling the enormity of it all. Indeed it just seems incredible to me that something – someone, even – cannot even exist 33 weeks ago and yet be ready to pop out into the world and be a fully functional human being nine months down the line.

The more I have been thinking about this the more it has been messing with my mind. Maybe writing it down will help me to get a better handle on it all.

Bear with me.

Bump is the direct result of one of my sperm joining with one of Sally's eggs. Before that happened, there was no Bump; there was only sperm and egg. And this is how it was with me. I didn't exist 38 years ago; 'I' was just a collection of DNA inside my Dad's sperm and my Mum's egg.

This is how it is with everyone. Moreover, this is how it has always been, ever since life as we know it came into being.

Whilst this kind of existentialist nonsense can really do your head in after a while (especially when it stops you from sleeping), it does make you think about the enormity of the concept we know as 'life'.

I tried to share this with Sal the other evening but I could tell from the glazed-over look in her eyes that it would be to no avail (she can't even watch loveable hippy musician-turned-physicist Professor Brian Cox on telly for more than five minutes so I really should have known better). Nevertheless I explained that I had come to see life as being a bit like the Olympic torch relay, i.e. the DNA of human beings gets passed from two individual adults to one little person in much the same way as the Olympic flame gets passed from one torch bearer to another.

However, I have come to the conclusion that the people and the torches are actually just transient containers; vessels if you like. When a torch completes the part it has to play in the relay, it gets extinguished. The flame that it carried on the other hand continues to burn brightly in a different torch. A different vessel.

And that's how it is with us.

Each and every one of us is a vessel. Whilst we each have our own personalities, characteristics and agendas; we all incubate the flame of life within us. Of course, we each have the choice of whether or not to pass that flame on to another vessel.

And I think this is the best part.

This flame that has been burning within me (and Sal) for thirty-odd years will soon get to reside in a brand new custodian. This person, quite unknowingly, will take possession of an energy force (I'm sorry but I don't know what else to call it) that has been around since time immemorial and will one day hopefully pass it on to little vessels of her own.

Isn't that wonderful?

We often think of ourselves as being significant members of family dynasties that have roots stretching back hundreds of years. Indeed, lots of people research their family trees these days in order to establish exactly where their fore-bearers came from (my uncle did it; turns out my dad's family came from the north west of Ireland).

The truth is though, we are not as important as we would like to think we are. We are merely containers, temporal cargo ships carrying a cargo which is far more important than any individual vessel.

We each carry within us the spark of life, the origin of the human being. Without getting too scientific (and I freely admit that I don't understand it all myself) this origin goes back long before apes started walking upright or Adam rogered Eve in the Garden of Eden. It is thought that life on Earth first began at the bottom of the oceans nearly 4 billion years ago in the form of simple organic compounds. Over time, these simple compounds evolved into more complicated organisms and branched off into numerous different species, some of which eventually left the oceans to live on land. In the millennia that followed, these myriad forms of life developed into dinosaurs, crocodiles, elephants, whales, owls, ants, swans and apes as well as a million other living things.

Unlike the swans and the elephants, the apes got bored of living in their natural environment and had some kind of innate ambition to improve their lot. So, just for a laugh, they stopped living in trees and started walking upright as they thought this would increase their chances of evolving into highly intelligent creatures who would one day be capable of sitting all day in front of a computer screen and then sitting all night in front of the telly.

But where did the elements (and energy) needed to create these simple organic compounds come from in the first place?

Well that's even more incredible.

All of the key elements that are present on Earth, such as carbon, nitrogen and oxygen were first created in stars more than 4.5 billion years ago. These elements were effectively the building blocks of everything on Earth and helped to turn what was essentially just a big rock into a planet capable of supporting life.

Because humans and every other animal on Earth contain these elements, it is fair to say (as Carl Sagan once famously did) that "We are made of star stuff."

How cool is that? The flame that burns within us, the origin of life, is literally stardust.

As far as cargos go, this a pretty special one to carry. To be able to pass it on feels – at this moment in time anyway – like a supreme honour.

Author's note: as unlikely as it may sound, no drugs of any kind were smoked during the writing of this chapter.

5

Without wanting to sound too melodramatic; I think this shit just got real. After the whimsical and slightly trippy mind wandering of last week, I now feel as though the main event is really just around the corner.

There are a number of reasons for this.

The first is that Sally informed me that now is the time for Bump to 'engage', i.e. move herself into an upside down position so that she will be ready to pop out head-first when the time comes.

The second is that this could be any time now.

That's right, Sally could go into labour right this minute as - according to Sal's pregnancy books - Bump is now developed enough to live outside of the womb. Moreover, the 'Week 34' chapter I read last night went into quite a bit of detail about recognising the onset of labour and identifying contractions.

Surely this can't be right? We've not even been to our antenatal classes yet?

Whilst I wouldn't say this has caused me to panic as such, I do feel like I'm standing at battle stations now. In fact, I feel like Charlie Sheen at the beginning of *Platoon* when he's mulling over the prospect of finally joining the war he always wanted to fight in. And it's not just me; Sal too is a little alarmed by our new DefCon level.

She told me that she got a little freaked out when she saw a week-old baby the other day as she realised she will have one of her own in seven weeks time (or less). She also told me that she has been reading a bit about what happens if the baby doesn't engage and is more than a little worried about this happening.

Apparently, there are two ways to turn babies that don't engage before labour. The first is to physically manipulate them from the outside and the second is to have a Caesarean. Sal told me that her midwife said the Caesarean is often the best way to go in this situation as the other option carries the risk of wrapping the umbilical cord around the baby's neck.

Bump has been kicking like a Thai boxer this past day or so, so maybe this is a sign that she is endeavouring to get herself into a nice streamlined position for a stress-free exit. That is what I have been telling Sal at least as I don't want her to dwell too much on things that may not be issues.

Hopefully this is something we will not have to deal with.

Although slightly different to the examples listed above, something else happened this week which ramped up the reality of our situation another notch - the bungalow has quite suddenly become pink and girlyfied. The main reason for this is that Sally's elder sister Tina has given us some of her daughter Lily's old toys for Bump to play with when she gets older.

Amongst other things, there is a baby doll in pink dress; a motorised pink swing which the baby doll (dressed in pink) can be rocked in; a pink pram that the doll (and a friend – it's a double) can be pushed around in, and a pink fluffy cat which folds out into a pink pillow. Sally absolutely loves them all and says she cannot wait to play 'dollies' with Bump when she is older.

No disrespect to Tina but I don't like them at all (although I think Sally and Clare may have bought most of them for Lily in the first place). They are just far too pink and far too girly. I don't like pink and I think girls' toys in general are just a bit rubbish.

Surely toys are meant to be about fun, excitement and adventure. Think about it: a Scalextric is fun and exciting; a radio controlled tank is adventurous and cool. Looking after a dolly isn't fun or exciting. If anything it is the opposite as it teaches kids to be responsible and look after others rather than race recklessly and wage war.

I ask you where is the fun in that?

So not only am I having a baby very, very soon; I'm having a child that will - if Sally gets her way - be dressed like Tinkerbell and have a bedroom like Barbara Cartland's parlour.

Perhaps panic is the right word after all.

I don't really know how to explain it. I still feel like I'm ready for it all to happen; everything just seems so much more serious now. I mean, I could have a daughter lying next to me (probably in a pink outfit) this time next week. It's not far off any more. It's not something that's going to happen next season. It's going to happen soon; very soon maybe.

Without doubt – this shit just got very real.

6

Well, despite my hopes/fears, there is no little baby girl lying next to me as I type this. Everything seems to be going in the right direction with regards to Bump engaging though as Sal was told by a stand-in midwife that our baby girl has indeed started to turn. Whilst I immediately regarded this as being good news, Sally seemed a little disappointed when she told me. When I asked her why she wasn't thrilled, she simply said:

"If I'd needed a C-section then we could have had her a week earlier."

I thought about this for a bit. Whilst I am almost as keen as Sal is for this pregnancy-to reach its climax, I don't want her to go through a Caesarean if it can be helped. Sal seems quite matter of fact about the prospect of having her belly cut open (as do many other women I have spoken to about it) but I feel that a birth should be as natural as possible, in so far as it doesn't pose a risk to the mother or child.

Anyway, this remains somewhat unresolved as Sally isn't convinced Bump has really turned or engaged. The fact that the breadth of her belly is pretty solid and the stand-in midwife had her in and out of the examination room within five minutes is causing her to question things.

Fortunately, the person who will be taking us for our first antenatal class is Sally's regular mid-wife (Mary) so she will get her to 'have a quick feel' when we go and see her next week.

I'm still not sure what to expect from these classes. My only real knowledge of them comes from what I have seen on films and sit-coms, i.e. earth-mothers/man-haters using collective nouns and asking attendees to 'share their aspirations' as they do breathing exercises with conscientious vegetarians.

If they are like this then they are likely to be the longest one-and-a-half hours of my life as I really cannot stand New-Age nonsense that goes well beyond the pale of simply being open-minded. I am always keen to learn and am generally very receptive to new ways of thinking; however I have an immediate and deeply ingrained antipathy towards anything resembling a corporate team-building exercise or interview ice-breaker so it is fair to say I have more than a degree of reticence about the whole thing.

Needless to say, it is not all about me so it doesn't matter how nauseating the experience might be, I need to get involved and absorb the stuff they're going to throw at us. The first class (first of two) is all about labour and pain relief so it is pretty important I learn everything I can, especially if Bump really has started to turn and is counting down the days to the moment she will pop out like Thunderbird Four.

Whilst Sally and I have talked about things like antenatal classes, labour, childcare and feeding (and many other things of course) over the past few weeks, we have not mentioned Bump's fingers for some time. Indeed, it felt like quite a bolt from the blue when she brought up the subject - seemingly from nowhere - a couple of nights ago. It's strange because it's not like I have consciously put it to the back of my mind; it's just that it seems to have taken something of a back seat in recent weeks. Maybe it's because I have been worrying about my ever-precarious freelancer income and have been spending more time searching for jobs online as a result.

Whatever the reason, I felt all those same emotions - sadness, frustration, sympathy, anger - run through me in double-quick time when Sal said, 'it's such a shame about her hand' after a programme we were watching on telly came to an end the evening before last.

After pausing to process what she had said, I instinctively told her 'It'll be alright, Sal.'

'I know', she said; and with that she lolloped off to the toilet to go through her prolonged routine of nightly ablutions.

As she did that, I went and sat in the garden and let my mind wander. As I looked up at the perfectly clear night sky, I considered how unbelievable it was that we had managed to not talk about something so important for so long.

I know that I have had dreams about Bump's little hand and have thought about her fingers whenever I held Finley in my arms (which has been quite a lot lately). I can also be pretty sure that similar things wouldn't have been too far from Sally's thoughts either.

So why hadn't we spoken about it for so long?

I guess the rational and objective answer would be that our subconscious selves concluded there was nothing we could do to affect the situation so talking over issues we had talked over a hundred times before would be of little use.

Makes sense. But that didn't make me feel any better as I sat there looking up at the stars. I know I'm not a bad person but for some reason I felt like a guilt-ridden, eighteen-carat shit at that moment. After what seemed like an eternity, Sally emerged from the bathroom looking twice as tired as when she went in. Standing in the hallway I gave her a cuddle and reiterated that everything would be alright.

'I know', she said, 'She'll be OK.'

And then the feeling of being a thoroughly contemptible bastard was gone; just like that. It would be nice to sum up these feelings, and their significance, in a nice little paragraph and impart a few words of wisdom in the process. But the truth is this pregnancy seems to be producing moments when my hormones quite unexpectedly torment my soul for what seems like no apparent reason at all. Times when incredibly potent pangs of raw emotion pierce my heart like a matador's spear in a bull's neck. It has happened before but this was the first time I actually felt aware of it occurring as a distinct moment in time.

And I can't for the life of me work it out at all.

7

It's official: Bump is engaged, primed and ready for action.

We know this because Sally's midwife Mary gave her a quick once over after our first antenatal class on Thursday. Her little head is upside down and her little backside is sticking up in the middle of Sal's belly - all systems are go!

How cool is that!

I was particularly pleased to hear this as the description Mary gave of Caesarean births during our one-and-a-half hour of 'Labour & Pain Relief' made me wince at times.

The class itself was actually okay. There were only nine of us at the Children's Centre in all: two other couples (who were about our age), a woman on her own, a student nurse and Mary, the midwife.

Mary is what London media types would refer to as a 'salt of the earth Northerner', a woman who speaks frankly, tells it like it is and doesn't bother with heirs and graces. I warmed to her immediately.

She is one of those people who makes you feel at ease straight away; not because she is a trained healthcare professional but because she is just a very down-to-earth character. Although she doesn't look like her physically, she reminds me a bit of Nurse Gladys Emmanuelle from the popular 1970s TV show, *Open All Hours* (she actually looks a bit like a slightly larger version of Sophie from *Peep Show*).

The class itself was very straightforward. At the beginning, Mary asked us what we would like to know and got the student nurse to list our questions in bulletin form on a flipchart. After a very short time, a comprehensive list was composed of topics ranging from 'how will I know when to go to hospital' and 'what drugs can I take' to 'should I have an epidural' and 'what about parking?' (she looked at me when she read this one out; it was like she was reading my mind).

After moving our chairs into a circle and getting a fan brought in to take some of the heat out of the small room, Mary talked us through each issue in detail, adding L. S. Lowry-type diagrams on the flipchart where necessary.

The most important thing I learnt in the first quarter of an hour was that having more than three contractions in ten minutes is the sign that everything is green for go and that your lady should be on her way to hospital. Mary also rattled on about waters breaking and smelling of spunk but the main thing I took in was that one key nugget of information: three or more contractions in ten minutes means it's time to get Sal to hospital. Check.

The next thing of note was regarding pain and pain relief.

Mary told us that, whilst some ladies find giving birth to be a pleasurable experience, most consider it to be the most fearfully painful thing that ever has or ever will happen to them. Therefore, partners (she looked at each of us men in turn) should 'appreciate this' when their girlfriends/wives tear into them with language that would make Malcolm Tucker blush. Sally looked at me and smiled at this point. Surely the sweet girl behind those saintly blue eyes would never utter a harsh word about me in public – not sober anyway.

Fortunately, there are all kinds of drugs and other pain relief measures available so there are always options available if the pain gets too much. I was surprised to hear that some of the better known pain relief measures were actually derivatives of morphine. Mary said that she had one of these options when she was in labour and that she swore a handsome firefighter came to keep her company in the room for a while soon after it was administered.

This led us nicely on to epidurals and spinal blocks. These numb the pain of labour completely yet allow ladies to stay conscious. That sounds pretty good I thought. Why don't all women have them?

Mary was looking at me as I was thinking this. 'The Force' was clearly strong with her and my thoughts had betrayed me. Within a matter of seconds she pulled some kind of medical item out of her 1970s pregnancy paraphernalia bag and passed it round for us all to have a look at. It was a needle tip, the type they use to inject women with an epidural or spinal block.

The thing about this needle tip though is that it wasn't the length of those needles you see when giving blood or getting travel jabs; it was HUGE! If Warwick Davies had a bespoke jousting lance made then there wouldn't be much difference between it and the pre-packaged giant spear of death that was being passed around us at that time.

I was completely transfixed by this seemingly legal instrument of torture so the rest of what Mary had to say didn't all go in. I think I heard her say that some ladies also have to have a catheter fitted when they opt for an epidural or spinal block so that is something else that needs to be considered.

I tried to imagine what it would be like to be in so much pain that you would gladly relieve yourself into a bag in front of perfect strangers whilst someone else you don't know plunges a needle the size of a dwarf's bespoke medieval weapon into your lower back

Why don't all women have them??

I could see in her eyes that Mary knew what I was thinking. Was she Jedi or Sith..?

There were some lighter points in proceedings though, such as when we talked about what to pack in your hospital bag. As well as expected items like sanitary towels, baby clothes, front opening nighties and a camera; Mary also advised ladies to 'have a lunch packed for their poor fellas'. She pointed out that, while labour can be long and boring, men don't normally feel comfortable leaving their partners to go and get a bite to eat as they are fearful something will happen while they are away.

Like it. Check.

So all in all, the class was actually much better than I was expecting it to be. I must admit that I was a little disappointed we didn't get to lie on the floor and puff at each other like horny asthmatics, but it is fair to say I enjoyed it far more than I thought I would.

The children's centre it was held in is also only five minutes walk from our bungalow so it may turn out to be somewhere we'll visit once Bump makes an appearance. I know that Sal is very keen to get involved with mother & baby-type groups so this place could be just the ticket. Before we left, Mary told us that, amongst its many parent

& toddler group offerings, the Children's Centre hosts a 'Dads & babies' morning on Saturdays where fellas with little 'uns can come and get together to chat about fatherhood over bacon rolls.

I thought about it for a while and decided that it actually sounded like quite a good idea. After all, there aren't many places that do a decent bacon roll around here...

8

I am finding it a little difficult to write this entry as I have the twin distractions of the Hoover and the washing machine pounding in my ears (you can't escape the noise when you live in a bungalow). Funnily enough, noises of this kind have become a common feature since Sal finished work on Wednesday. In fact, I don't think there are many things which she hasn't felt the urge to clean, repair, move or throw out over the last few days (Smudge – quite wisely - has permanently decamped to the relative safety of the garden to stay away from her).

Fortunately, Mary threw some light on this behaviour when we went to our second antenatal class on Thursday. Apparently, lots of pregnant women get an innate urge to sort out their surroundings and make sure everything is ready when they are close to dropping – this is known as 'nesting'.

The thing is; Sally's pragmatist/utilitarian character ensures that she is a constant 'fusser' at the best of times. Priming her with some kind of intrinsic compulsion to nest is like feeding a flatulent pensioner with beans and broccoli: it's just too much.

The second of our two antenatal classes ('Caring for your baby') was actually a lot shorter than the first. Moreover, the two male partners who came last week gave it a wide berth this week so I was the only man there (there was only me, Sal, Mary, the student nurse and two of the three other pregnant women).

Perhaps because of this, Mary seemed to go into more detail about things which most men don't normally get to hear discussed in polite society. To be sure, she didn't hold back at all when she told us how some doctors in the Middle East carry out procedures which ensure women who give birth there can still be 'nice and tight' for their men afterwards. She also seemed to go into far more detail than was necessary about her own dealings with the menopause (though I didn't really understand how this was relevant to the topic).

Nevertheless, she did give us plenty of useful information about things like bringing baby home, feeding and changing nappies. The pooing side of things was a real eye-opener as we learnt how a baby's faeces can change from jet-black (and tar-like) to green to yellow at various stages during its young life.

I must admit that the prospect of wiping up green or yellow turds made gag a little bit.

We also learnt that, whilst midwives and healthcare professionals are of course impartial and we should in no way feel obliged to subscribe to their own personal opinions at all, breast feeding is far and away and without any shadow of a doubt the very best option available when it comes to feeding a baby.

After speaking with Clare and Tina, Sally had already decided that bottle feeding was likely to be the best option for her so I knew she would be less than enthused by what she was hearing. The reasoning behind this is that having bottles will allow us to share the feeding duties and relieve Sal of the need to be a milking machine.

To be fair, Mary did make a good case for breast-feeding. I had no idea that breast milk helps to line a new born baby's innards with nutrients when it first arrives in the outside world, or that it provides them with greater resistance against things like osteoporosis later on in life. However, one quick glance over at Sal told me that she was having none of it.

That's my girl; swim against the stream!

Toward the end of the class, Mary told us that she (or a member of her team) would come round and visit us at home a few times after Bump had arrived and that other health visitors would come and check on us even further down the line.

As she gave us some handouts and contact detail forms to fill in, I considered (not for the first time) just how fortunate we are in this country to have a comprehensive healthcare system that provides care of this kind for free. Every eligible citizen in the UK regardless of whether they have been resident here for a year or their whole lives - can get the medical advice and support they need simply by picking up the phone or visiting their local GP. Think about it; every pregnant woman (and her partner) in the UK can expect – expect - to get fully qualified guidance and treatment before, during and after the arrival of their baby without having to pay a penny. There aren't that many Western countries that are willing to meet expectations of this kind so I think our healthcare system is something we should all be very proud of.

As we walked back to the car after the lesson had finished, I asked Sally whether her thoughts on breast feeding had changed.

'Well', she began, 'I think I'll try it for a few days at least; give our little girl the mummy milk she needs to get a good start. I reckon bottles will be the way forward after that though'.

I looked at her and smiled my approval.

'I can't think why...' she added, '...But I almost feel guilty for saying that'. 'Really?' I replied 'How strange!'

Two days later, Sally and I sat down in our show home-like living room, tucked into some lovely home-baked sausage rolls and had a conversation which we both acknowledged was long overdue – what to name our baby.

We had touched fleetingly on this really quite important subject a number of times over the past eight months but for some reason we had never actually taken the time to talk it through properly. The only thing we had decided on was that she was going to have my surname. I didn't push overly hard for this. In fact, I had told her that a double-barrelled name was fine with me (for a girl, anyway) but she wasn't keen on that and finally decided she was okay with our little one taking my surname.

My basic criteria for a choice of name was that it needed to be something I would feel comfortable shouting at a naughty two-year old in a packed supermarket. I remember years ago hearing a flustered, well-to-do father on holiday in Greece yelling 'Tarquin, put your bloody suncream on!' at his son and immediately thinking, 'What. A. Twat.'

Sal's criterion was far simpler; she simply wanted our little girl to have a name that sounded nice. After a relatively short amount of time, we both agreed that 'Ellie' was a name we both liked. I liked it because it was pretty, modern and sounded like something I would be happy to reach the 50 decibel mark with in Tesco. Sally liked it because Bump kicked her when she said it out loud.

Well that was pretty easy I thought. Unbeknownst to me, that was actually the easy bit. Now that we had a first and last name, we needed to put the meat in the sandwich; the middle name.

What followed was a painstakingly slow exercise that involved us both looking blankly up at the ceiling and trying to remember every female we had ever met. Once one came into our minds, we would say it out loud and wait for the other to give it a 'yay' or 'nay'. To observers, we must have looked like two pot-heads playing the most convoluted game of *Guess Who* ever.

After what seemed like an age of trying to find a name of either one or three syllables which would be phonetically compatible with the names it followed and preceded, we eventually decided that we needed help from a higher power. And so we turned to the one omnipotent force on this planet that can provide light where there is darkness; wisdom where there is ignorance.

Google.

But even the might and power of the world's foremost digital intelligence gatherer could not save the day. Despite providing us with literally thousands of traditional, contemporary, Scandinavian, Arabian, exotic, astronomical, spiritual and mythical girls' names; we couldn't find a single middle name that we both agreed sounded right. And that's how we left it.

Feeling somewhat frustrated that our name-finding endeavours didn't yield more in the way of success; I decided to put on my shoes and take a customary walk around the block. As I shut the door behind me and zipped up my top, I heard a clattering-type noise followed by a gentle hum. Just to be on the safe side, I reopened the door and shouted to Sal to ensure she was okay.

But she couldn't hear me with the Hoover on...

9

And so we have reached August. August is always a month I look forward to as it heralds the arrival of that most enjoyable (and frustrating) of pursuits – Fantasy Football. Of course, August is extra special this year as it will provide me with a far more important arrival – my daughter. Regardless of whether Ellie Bump is early or late, this is the month she will arrive.

This is the month I will become a dad.

For the sake of melodrama I would like to report that Sally and I have been on tenterhooks the whole time and that the tension is killing us both. However, the truth is that things have actually been pretty chilled-out. Whilst we are both quite aware that 'the event' could kick-off at any given time, we are both going about our daily lives as we normally would. Sally fills her weekdays with *Homes Under the Hammer* , naps on the sofa and trips out with Clare and

Finley whilst I spend most of my time applying for jobs online and doing the relatively little work currently available to me. After tea, we will more than likely go for a leisurely walk around the park before watching a bit of telly and drifting off to bed around the ten o'clock mark (for Sal that is; 10pm is now my established start time for two uninterrupted hours on PlayStation).

So, really; rather than walking on eggshells and fretting about the weasel going pop (not that I'm calling Sal a weasel), we are simply keeping calm and carrying on. I think the reason for this pervading sense of calm is two-fold. The first factor is that I'm not someone who is prone to worrying much anyway; and the second is that we really couldn't be more prepared than we already are.

As well as having the nursery all sorted, the name chosen (still no middle name, mind) and Sally's hospital bag all packed; we now have a Moses basket positioned at the foot of our bed and a baby seat fitted in Sal's car (as well as a separate base in my car – just in case). We even have a nappy-changing station set up and some spare batteries and a charger on call in the kitchen to ensure our camera has plenty of juice for those all-important first photos!

We couldn't be more ready, and I am pretty sure it is this, rather than my stoic-like propensity to act like Mr Spock whenever the shit hits the fan, which is enabling Sal to feel so relaxed about everything at the moment.

And she really is relaxed. Indeed, I might even go so far as to say I don't think I have seen her this laid-back at any other point during the pregnancy. Whilst the fact she no longer has to go to work undoubtedly has a lot to do with it, I suspect that having the finishing line in sight is probably the key factor. She really has been through the ringer over the past eight months so I can see why the prospect of being so close to the end would give her a positive charge.

She is excited and so am I. The vibe within our bungalow is really positive right now, much like it was at the very beginning of the pregnancy all those months ago. Despite all that's happened and all that is likely to happen with her hand, the thought of having our very own baby girl knocking about the place is palpably enthusing. Without wanting to sound too sickly sweet, life just feels pretty darn good right now.

To try and make ourselves even more prepared, Sal and I went through some of the handouts given to us by Mary at the Children's Centre. As well as numerous pages about why 'breast is best' there were some poorly photocopied pages that showed positions women in the various stages of labour can adopt to relive contraction-related pain and discomfort. Most of them resembled instalments from the Amish version of the Karma Sutra and didn't look like the kinds of positions Sally would be able to pull off even without a baby in her belly.

After scrutinising the images for a relatively short time, we finally decided that there were only really three that seemed genuinely doable: the one that involved leaning against a wall like you were counting to a hundred for a game of Hide & Seek; the one that involved adopting a 'doggy-style' position over a chair seat and rocking your arse from side to side (my favourite); and the one where you sit on the toilet but put a few cushions around it to make it feel a bit more comfy. Whilst the 'Hide and Seek' and toilet offerings pretty much spoke for themselves, we thought we should at least give the bending over position a try. So I put a few cushions on top of Sally's beloved pouffe and she gingerly got down on her knees and manoeuvred herself into a position where she was leaning on the pouffe for support. Once she had scrunched up the cushions and got herself completely comfortable, I started rubbing the base of her spine as I remembered Mary saying this would help during the early stages.

'How is that?' I asked.

'D'you know what? That actually feels quite nice'.

And so I carried on for a minute or so, massaging the small of her back with the base of my palm in a circular motion.

'Yeah, that feels good', she said looking for all the world like she was about to drop off. 'Why don't you try rocking your bum from side to side?' I ventured.

'My pelvis you mean?'

'Whatever, just rock something and see if it helps'

And so, with the smallest amount of effort possible, Sally duly wiggled her bottom from side to side with all the gusto of a hedgehog moving house.

'Try rubbing my back at the same time', she said.

So there we were; Sally bent over the pouffe wiggling her derriere like a Babesation 'model' on the late shift and me massaging her back like a perverted chiropractor. Looking at Sal I noticed she had scrunched up her eyes quite tightly. In fact, she looked as though she was in a bit of discomfort. 'Any good?' I asked. 'Are you OK?' And with that, a bloody great tear of a noise, like Velcro being ripped from Velcro, came thundering out of Sally's swaying bottom. 'Much better', she said, turning her head to grin at me with a reddened face. 'Thanks'.

Grotty trumper.

10

'You might want to get up...'

It's 8.16am and Sally is standing by the side of the bed, gently shaking my shoulder and sporting a curious look on her face.

'What? Why?' I stutter, somewhat bewildered.

Swaying gently from side to side and caressing Ellie bump with both hands she calmly says:

'I think it's started. I think I'm having contractions'.

'Are you certain', I ask. 'Are you sure you're not having those Higgs boson things that were in your book; those fake contraction jobbers?'

She scowls at me, irritated but not angry. 'My mucous plug has gone; I'm pretty sure this is the real thing!'

'This can't be right', I think to myself. 'She's not due for another week yet!' But, as I process the information I have just received and stare hypnotically at Sal's bump, my mind becomes polarised and one thing becomes crystal clear.

I won't be sorting out my Fantasy Football team today.

9.47am
After ascertaining how regular and painful her contractions are (not very), we conclude that Sal is in the very earliest stages of labour. She is in no real discomfort so we decide to do what her books recommended and go about our usual business. For Sal, that means getting settled down on the sofa for another thrilling episode of *Homes Under the Hammer* while for me it means trying to work out a way to accommodate Sergio Aguero and Wayne Rooney in the same team.

This is not how labour goes down in the films.

Just as Sal is getting comfy the phone rings. It is Clare.

'I haven't heard from you today; I thought you might be in labour'.

Uncanny.

10.34am
After eventually deciding to omit Rooney from my starting line-up altogether, I decide to time Sal's contractions again. They are still quite mild and are coming around seven minutes apart. All in all she is still very relaxed.

This is starting to feel a little bit surreal. It feels like we are in a play, acting out the roles of parents-to-be with all the enthusiasm of 14 year-old drama students in detention.

Midday
Time for another time check. Things are starting to progress a little further now as Sal is experiencing three contractions roughly every 13–14 minutes. She is still pretty chilled though and seems quite unperturbed as she munches her Hula Hoops and watches Eamon Holmes chat inanely to some gardening twins on *This Morning*.

Clare and Finley come knocking at 12.30pm. Although she is beside herself with excitement, Clare takes a moment to give her little sister some profound words of wisdom.

'It does hurt, Sal. It really does fucking hurt!'

Thanks for dropping by, Clare.

2.05pm
Now we're cooking! Sal's contractions are coming every 4-5 minutes and are beginning to hurt. As we note the times, one set of figures shows that she nearly has three contractions within ten minutes (the sign to go to hospital). Although this turns out to be a one-off, it sends a surge of adrenaline through me which feels like an electric shock.

This is happening. This is really happening!

We're going to have a baby!!

3.28pm
The pain is now such that Sal thinks it's time to make use of the TENS machine she rented off the midwives for £10. After looking through the user manual and sticking the pads to Sal's back, I turn on the little device to let it work its magic.

3.47pm
TENS machine is back in its box. Utter shite.

6.53pm
OK, we are really getting to the meat of things now. Sally is in such discomfort that she cannot help but scream out in pain with each contraction. Looking through the books, I conclude she is coming to the end of the early stage of labour and is on the cusp of the active part. However, her

contractions are still not frequent enough to go into hospital yet so she is having to 'grin and bear it' for the time being.

Sally flits between the Hide & Seek and 'Doggy over pouffe' pain relief positions but neither one seems to alleviate her discomfort more than the other. We even try 'Walking up a mountain' together (hugging each other standing up and walking on the spot) as this is meant to help compartmentalise the onset, apex and dissipation of the pain.

It doesn't.

She is in pain. She is ready. She needs to be in hospital.

9.06pm

Sally's very painful contractions are now coming on at a rate of three every 10 or 11 minutes. I convince her that now is the time to call the hospital and she does. After a worryingly long wait, a lady at the Maternity Department eventually answers the phone and rapidly quizzes Sally about her physical state. In between bouts of semi-stifled screaming, Sal relates all the information we have and acknowledges to the lady that we know we may have to come home if she is not dilated enough.

So that's it – we're going in!

9.54pm

Following a disappointingly sensible drive to the hospital (my one chance to run red lights and get a police escort; gone), we arrive at the seemingly deserted Triage part of the Maternity Department just before 10pm. After being buzzed in via an intercom, we sit in a small, empty waiting area and watch a succession of four heavily pregnant women and their defeated-looking partners leave through the double doors we just came in through. Sally doesn't take this to be a good omen – clearly this is one maternity department that enforces its 'not ready then go home' policy pretty stringently.

Twenty minutes later and we are in an assessment room with two cheery and seemingly quite busy female maternity nurses talking in hushed tones. There are four beds in the room, each of which is curtained off to provide those lying on them a little bit of privacy. Although I can hear machines beeping behind some of the other curtains, I think we are the only couple in here.

One of the women asks Sally to take off her leggings, lie on a bed and cover herself with a blanket. Within a matter of moments we are joined by a different nurse who explains how she is going to examine Sally and listen to the baby's heartbeat. At the end of her little spiel, she tells us that we will be going home if Sally's cervix has not dilated by more than 4cm.

We are not going home. Sally is now at 5cm and the baby's heart rate is exactly what it should be. Apparently, we couldn't have timed it any better.

We are green for go – it's time to have this baby!

10.46pm

With Sally now semi-dressed again, another nurse leads us down the corridor and round a corner to our room for the evening – a maternity-led delivery suite replete with big bouncy exercise ball, over-sized bean bag, two chairs, a foam bed, an en-suite toilet/wet room and a CD player from the early 1990s. Once inside, I immediately open the windows to let some cool air in.

Whilst I am bubbling over with nervous excitement, Sal

seems distracted; like there's something else she should be doing right now. Within a couple of seconds though she is tensed-up and screaming aloud, her mind once again focussed on the small matter of having a baby.

With this, a midwife comes into the room to assess Sal and check the baby's heartbeat. She is young and softly spoken and has a natural empathy which is so nice it would probably get on your nerves if you weren't experiencing a medical emergency. After directing Sal to make herself comfortable in whatever way she sees fit, our new best friend wheels over the gas and air trolley so that Sal can take the edge off her increasingly painful contractions.

And then she is gone, leaving us both alone again. Sal looks hot so I help her over to the seat nearest the open window. She is in between contractions as we do this and so is able to speak quite calmly and articulately. Once settled into the seat, another contraction comes on and Sal immediately reaches for the gas and air.

As she takes a deep breath and exhales out the pain, the mouth-piece of the gas and air resonates with a sound that is not unlike that of a large mammal announcing its arrival at a new watering hole. I'm not kidding, the noise coming out of Sal every five seconds sounds like something an elephant or rhino would make - although I choose not to mention this to her.

Bless her; she is really in some proper pain now. Quite out of the blue I think back to what Mary said in the parenting class about men feeling helpless when they have to watch their partners in labour. I can see that Sal is suffering and yet there is nothing I can do to make the pain go away. I'm also really conscious of not wanting to come out with trite things like 'take the gas and air' or 'breathe...' as I am pretty sure this won't help much. So, I just sit on the bed next to her and stroke her thigh, mumbling the odd 'well done' and 'you're doing so well' here and there. I like to think I'm helping in my own way but I don't think I am.

A different midwife enters the room. She too is young and softly spoken and gifted with a mumsy-like disposition. Again she checks the baby's heartbeat and assesses Sal's progress with a few 'yes or no' questions.

'Would you like some Pethidine?' she asks.

Sally - just off the back of another painful contraction - looks over at me before answering.

'What do you reckon?' I say, prompting her to give us an insight into how much pain she feels she's in right now

'I...I..I think I'll wait a bit longer. Just a bit longer', she stutters, already anticipating the onset of another wave of pain.

'In that case; would you like a nice cup of tea?'

You've got to love the NHS.

11.49pm

Sally is now slouched back in the super-sized bean bag with her feet on the floor and her legs slightly akimbo. I am sat on a chair beside her left shoulder while the gas and air trolley is standing guard next to her right. Despite yielding and opting to have some Pethidine pumped into her less than half an hour ago, Sally is now in extreme pain, screaming as loudly and as violently as I have ever heard her. The gas and air seems to be having no effect whatsoever and Sal seems to be taking it more out of habit than for its ability to relieve pain.

Both of the young midwives are in the room now, crouched on the floor either side of Sally's outstretched feet. After listening to the baby's heartbeat for the umpteenth time, the first midwife musters up her 'I mean business now' voice and says to Sal:

'What I want you to do now Sally is to not scream out when the next contraction comes. What I want is for you to channel the energy from that scream and push it out through your bottom, as if you were having a poo'.

Sally murmurs her approval and nods at me as she grabs my hand. Within ten seconds, Sally is screaming the place down with her loudest banshee call yet. Less than a minute later she is apologising in stutters and telling us all how she doesn't think she can cope. We all tell her how well she's doing and encourage her to 'have a really good shit'.

At this point, Sal looks up at me, either to seek out encouragement or to check to see I am still there. I smile back at her, kiss her hand and tell her she's doing wonderfully well. Another contraction is on its way; Sally has a mixed look of genuine fear and steely determination on her face.

This shriek is even louder than the last. Through the open window I can hear dogs barking. She is trying, bless her; she is trying to channel that energy through her backside but the pain is just too much for her to bear.

Again she apologises and again the midwives reassure her that all is well. One of them excuses herself and disappears outside for a couple of minutes. Upon returning she retakes her position in the stalls and holds up a long white stick with a hook on the end that looks a bit like a long, skinny toothbrush.

'Now Sally; we're not sure whether baby is ready to come or whether your waters need to be broken', says young midwife number one pointing to the hook on the end of the stick.

'I apologise Sally; this may be a bit uncomfortable but it's something I need to do'.

I stroke the back of Sal's head and try to reassure her that this will all be worth it in the end. Not being able to speak anymore because of the severe discomfort she is in, Sally chooses to suck on some gas and air as the midwife goes down below with her sinister looking aqua tool.

Sally makes some slightly different noises now; more distressing than painful.

'I'm so sorry' says the midwife.

For the first time, I am starting to feel a bit worried. What if something is wrong? What if Sally needs to have a Caesarean? What if she doesn't make it through this? I grip her hand tightly as she moans and feel a lump in my throat as I do so.

Suddenly there is a noise like wet socks being dropped on linoleum.

Whapp!!

The young midwife's magic wand has done the trick. The water that was surrounding Ellie in her protective little sack is now all over the floor.

'There!' she says, and the way she says it makes me think we're over the last hurdle and into the final stretch. 'Okay Sally, what we're seeing now is that there is a little bit of poo mixed in with the water. This is quite normal, but it does mean that baby is a little bit distressed okay, so now I want you to push very hard so that we can get her out. Okay, I need you to push hard so that we can get Ellie out'.

Sally immediately looks up at me and I can see that the mention of the word 'distressed' has got her spooked.

I lean forward as far as I can and I kiss her repeatedly on her left temple.

'It's going to be just fine', I say in the most reassuring voice I can manage. 'All you need to do is push good and hard and our baby will be here'. As I lean back I can see the fear in her eyes. We're both scared. Something doesn't feel right.

Another contraction is coming. Sally squeezes my hand tighter than it has ever been gripped before.

'Push Sally. Push hard through your bottom!'

'AAAARRRRRGGGGGHHHHH!!!!'

Never before have I heard Sal scream this loud. Never before have I heard anyone scream this loud.

'That's good. And again!'

'NNNNNNNNNNHHHHHHHH!!!!!!!

AAAAAAARRRRRRRGGGGGHHHHH!!!!!'

Sally's fingernails are now tearing into my hand like cat's claws. Midwife number one edges forward once again and reaches beneath the blanket with one hand. 'Okay Sally, that's brilliant. What I want you to do now is push against my fingers down into your bottom'.

There is a palpable sense of electricity in the room. We all know that something is going to happen.

AAAAAAAAAAAHHHHHHHHHHH!!!!!!!
EEEEEEEEEEEEEEEEEEEEAAAAAAAAAAAAAH
HHHHHHHH!!!!

'That's it Sally. That's it!' says midwife number two leaning forward.

'Keeping pushing sweetheart' I say looking at the blanket. Keep pushing down!'

OOOOOOOEEEEEEAAAAAAHHHHHH!!!!!!!!
AAAAAAAAAAAAAHHHHH!!!!!
AHHHHHHHHHHH!

'You're doing so well Sally; you're so very nearly there'.

AAAAAAAARRRRRRGGGGGHHHHHHHH!!!

'Push! Push hard!'

AAAEEEEEAAAHHH!!!!

'Push Sal. Push sweetheart!!'

AAAAAAAAAAAAAAAAARRRRRRRRRRRRRRG
GGGGGGGGGGGGGGGHHHHHHHHHHHH!!!
!!!!!!!

I've lost all feeling in my hand but I don't care. I can hear crying. I can't see her but I can hear her crying. My daughter has arrived.

'Here she is!' says midwife number one popping up above the blanket like a Punch & Judy puppet.

Here she is. A brand new human being taking her very first breaths of fresh air. A whole new life coming to say hello to mummy and daddy.

The midwife wraps her up in some swaddling and passes her over to Sal so that she can experience some immediate 'skin-to-skin' time.

'And in double-quick time too' says midwife number two glancing up at the clock on the wall.

The time is 12.19am.

'We've only been in here an hour-and-a-half!'

12.20am

Within the space of 30 seconds, Sally's demeanour has changed from that of violent murder victim to accidental lottery winner. She is beaming – absolutely beaming. As I lean over to get a better look at our daughter I kiss Sal on the forehead and tell how proud of her I am.

And I really am. At this very moment I feel proud of everything and everyone. It's hard to explain but I feel like the whole world has done a good job tonight, like the stars have aligned and the Universe has declared a Bank Holiday for every living thing that has ever existed.

I don't think I have ever felt this good about anything before.

Despite all this however, I am not crying. I thought I would be but I'm not. Surprisingly enough, Sal isn't either. In many ways this has not been the end to the pregnancy I was expecting but that really doesn't matter. The only thing that matters is that Ellie is here and her mummy is okay.

Despite looking like she has done a triathlon, a marathon and a 'Tough Mudder' back-to-back, Sally looks remarkably well. To be sure, her blue eyes are dancing with delight.

Nestled in her arms and poking out of her swaddling, Ellie looks completely vulnerable and unbelievably lovely. As I watch her tiny little eyes trying to open and her bottom lip quivering away, I feel compelled to let her know that Daddy's here. And so I stroke the top of her head slowly and very deliberately with two fingers, beaming a smile to Sally and the midwives as I do so.

'She's lovely', says midwife number one.

'Yes', I say. 'She is'.

And now I'm completely and utterly lost. I've heard that people only see their life flash before them when they're sure they're about to die. At this moment though, as I'm running my fingers gently through a tiny little thatch of uneven hair on my daughter's head, I seem to be feeling, rather than seeing, my life flash before me. I feel like there should be some kind of emotionally charged song playing in the background – something by Coldplay, or Sigur Ros perhaps – as every strong feeling I have ever had seems to be rushing through my veins all at once.

This is what Doctor Who must feel like when he regenerates.

'Would you like to cut it?'

Midwife number two is looking up at me quizzically from

her half-crouching/kneeling position down by ground zero.

'Does Daddy want to cut the cord?'

'Oh yes' I reply. 'Definitely'.

The placenta had arrived during my out-of-body moment and now I actually had something to do. This was my contribution.

Midwife number two hands me an instrument which looks like the bastard child of a pair of scissors and secateurs and gestures whereabouts on the chord I need to be aiming for. The sinewy lifeline is actually a lot tougher than it looks and it takes a concerted effort for me to sever it in two.

The two midwives give me a muted cheer when I'm done and I feel suitably patronised. Well done me.

At this point, midwife number one picks Ellie up and takes her over to get weighed on a trolley with some digital scales on. It is at this point that I first see her little hand.

As I stand up to take a closer look, I can see that the hand is not how we expected it to be. The information we took from the scans at Addenbrookes hospital suggested that there would be a thumb, a forefinger and three fingers 'cut off' at the first joint.

From where I am standing now I can clearly see that, while the thumb looks 'normal', the index finger is significantly shorter than we expected, and the three other digits are nubbins.

'Six pounds, thirteen ounces', says the midwife. Ellie is

lifted from the scales, re-swaddled and brought back to mummy. Once suitably cradled, Sally gingerly uses her little finger to examine the digits and nubbins on Ellie's left hand.

As she is doing this, the thumb on the tiny hand moves. Seizing upon this, Sally moves her finger between Ellie's thumb and forefinger and is greeted with - a pinch.

We look at each other and smile broadly.

It works!

Her little hand has function. The thumb, the index finger and the muscles in the palm all work. Whilst I have no way of knowing for sure, I quickly conclude that, given time, she will more than likely be able to tie her shoe laces, eat with a knife and fork and hold a guitar plectrum; she will be able to grab hold of a swing, zip up a jacket and play 'catch'. Sure, she'll find these things – and a hundred other things besides – a little more difficult to do than most other kids, but she will be able to do them all the same.

Elation. Pure elation.

It doesn't seem fair that someone so unbelievably cute (she has my eyes and Sally's nose) should be saddled with any kind of hindrance; but, whilst Ellie's hand may well look different and be a little less capable than we were perhaps lead to believe, it somehow doesn't seem to matter at all.

Looking at her now nothing matters. I am completely smitten. She is gorgeous. Absolutely gorgeous.

2.01am

I am absolutely knackered now. The adrenaline is starting to ebb away and the events of the day are beginning to catch up with me. I have just spent the last 45 minutes feeding Ellie with a bottle of the hospital's SMA while the midwives put Sally on some kind of Y-shaped bed contraption and sewed up her traumatised front-bottom.

To her credit, Sally did try and feed Ellie on the breast before sending me to ask for a bottle. Indeed, she spent a good while trying to get her to latch on but our little girl was having absolutely none of it. To be fair, the nipple on Sal's left puppy is about half the size of Ellie's foot so how is she supposed to get her laughing gear around that? It would be like me trying to suck juice out of the end of a watermelon.

With the hub-bub and commotion of a few hours ago now well and truly over, Sally, Ellie and I lie back in our respective positions – Sally in bed, me in my trusty chair and Ellie in her mum's arms – and rest.

Sally and Ellie are going to be moved to the maternity ward soon where they'll spend the night. I am not permitted to stay over so I will have to go home and come back in the morning.

As I start to drift away, my mind gets to thinking about my mum and dad. I wonder if this is how my dad felt when I was born. I wonder if my mum and dad felt as scared and proud as Sal and I do now. It's going to be such a lovely moment when they meet their new granddaughter.

3.37am

I wanted to finish off this entry by writing something touching, life-affirming and wise. The truth is though; I am so knackered I can hardly string a sentence together. We have said goodbye and given our sincerest thanks to the midwives (they were fantastic) and are pushing Ellie - still sound asleep in her little transparent cot atop its wheeled trolley - to the maternity ward.

A short walk later and we are at the maternity ward reception area. The weary-looking ladies behind the desk smile at Sal then look me up and down in a way that makes me feel like I'm 17 and trying to get in a Ritzy nightclub.

'I'm afraid you won't be able to stay' says the elder of the two guardians, her tone much softer than I imagined it would be.

I nod my compliance and transfer Sally's bag from my shoulder to a waiting orderly.

'You'll come first thing in the morning?' Sal asks.

'First thing', I say.

She gives me a big hug then steps back and smiles: 'Would you like to say goodnight to your daughter?'

I smile slowly, lean lazily over Ellie's little see-through bed and run my fingers across her forehead.

'Night, night', I say. 'Daddy will see you tomorrow'.

And with that they are led through some double doors to get some well earned rest.
I wipe my eyes, take out my car keys and start walking down the corridor toward the exit.

'You'll be wanting this, won't you?'

Turning around I see the elder of the two gatekeepers holding a piece a paper aloft.

'Fill out this form and you won't have to pay full price for your parking'.

'You know what..?', I say, walking back to the desk to get my reward.

'What?', she says, now propping her head up with her other hand

'Today really has been a good day...'

EPILOGUE

Ellie celebrated her second birthday a few weeks ago. It's hard to imagine that it's been 24 months since she came into the world – to us it seems like just yesterday. For me personally I have found the past two years to be the most incredible and rewarding of my entire life. Don't get me wrong, they have also been the most stressful, frustrating and downright tiring years as well, but it is fair to say the pros have outweighed the cons completely.

I must admit though, Sal and I both felt a little lost when we took Ellie home all those months ago. That moment when we got back from the hospital, put her in her little 'Teddy Bed' in the living room and sat down on the sofa was priceless:

'So what do we do now??' Indeed.

I remember I felt quite self-conscious during the first couple of days. Whenever people like my Mum, Jan, Clare or Tina came round, I felt sure they were looking at me to see if I was holding Ellie correctly or feeding her in the right way. Of course, this subsided quickly enough as her many and varied demands soon made it clear appearances counted for nothing in this game.

To me the first six months or so of being a parent was like some kind of special forces training course: doing the same tasks over and over again and being deprived of sleep while your tormentor yelled, yelled and yelled some more...

It wasn't easy and there were more than a couple of times when I lost my composure and had to be 'subbed out' of the game by Sal who – bless her - was meant to be enjoying a few hours' respite. Night times were definitely the worst as Ellie needed feeding every four hours or so and was a right little terror at going to sleep, even when we sang to her for ages and shone her favourite light show projector on the ceiling.

When she wasn't crying, pooing or feeding though she was completely mesmerising. Tea times were the highlight of each day as it was around this time that we put some music on (usually *The Beatles*) and spread out a really fluffy rug on the floor for her to lie down on. She was especially lucid during these times and seemed to love fitting around to John, Paul, George and Ringo's melodic harmonies. I would look into her eyes and she would gaze back, giggling and smiling away with pure joy.

I absolutely loved tea times

Like most babies, Ellie started getting itchy feet during the second half of her first year. Bored with lying down all day and night, she started rolling around with more vigour, desperate to find a way to mobilise herself so that she could try and grab Smudge's tail.

We thought that she might struggle a little in this department with her smaller hand and modest grip. We needn't have worried. Within a relatively short time, Ellie was shuffling, plodding and eventually motoring around the living room on all fours without any problems whatsoever. Next was standing. Again we thought that things like pulling herself up so that she could lean against the sofa, or hold on to her walk-along pram might be a little beyond her. Right on cue though, she proceeded to clamber up anything and everything that she couldn't headbutt out of her way.

We even thought that some of her toys might be a little too contrived to handle. Granted, she found it difficult to manipulate some of the more cumbersome offerings but, on the whole, she simply adjusted her hand to accommodate whatever it was that she wanted to touch/bash/smash/chew on.

Needless to say, all of these developments have been amazing to watch. When she was less than ten-months old she managed to hold a ball upside down in her left hand by simultaneously engaging her thumb and forefinger with the bank of muscle on the left side of her palm. I think it was at this point that I thought to myself: "Yep. She's going to be just fine".

As you may have noticed, I absolutely love being a dad. I love the hugs, I love the playing around and I love the responsibility. On a deeper level I love how becoming a father seems to have opened up a whole new level of perception that was dormant within me before. Seriously, it is like I'm now seeing the world in colour after a lifetime of looking at things in black and white. I know this sounds a little bit New Age traveller but it's true; looking at things from a parent's 'we' point of view rather than an exclusively 'I' vantage point makes the world look and feel like a completely different place.

Before Ellie came along, I used to watch humanitarian news reports on the news and then put them to the back of my mind ten minutes after they'd finished airing. Now when I see images of families ravaged by famine, struggling through a pandemic or fleeing war my insides turn over and over for hours on end. Seeing reports of the things ISIS do to nine-year-girls, or the way young schoolgirls in some of our inner cities have been groomed makes me feel like picking up a gun and delivering some very old-school justice of my own. I even had tears in my eyes at the end of a rather moving episode of *DIY-SOS* the other week!

I never used to feel like this. Now I feel completely and utterly engaged with the world and I know it's down to the fact I am a father.

So what type of little girl is Ellie now? Well, the first thing to note is that our tiny little bundle of joy has grown into quite a force of nature. As well as being pretty tall (she is nearly as big as Finley already) and persistently full of beans, she can be supremely stubborn and incredibly independent-minded. Whilst this can prove somewhat frustrating at times, i.e. when she doesn't want to have her nappy changed, I can't help but think these characteristics will stand her in good stead later on in life.

She does pretty much everything a two-year-old girl does and it's wonderful to see. She plays on the swings at the play park, picks daisies for her mummy during the summer, and uses a spoon and fork to cover herself in spaghetti hoops at lunch time. In addition, she uses her pincer grip to hold onto the handlebars of her little stabilised trike and grip a plectrum when strumming/vandalising my guitar.

It may be that her stubbornness, wilfulness and strength of mind have helped to play a part in all this. Or it may just be like the doctors said all those months ago: that young children are excellent at adapting their physical capabilities to suit new situations. Perhaps it's a combination of both. Regardless though, she has already exceeded all of our expectations and I can't tell you how pleased and proud that makes me feel.

Of course, Sal and I both know that we are enjoying something of a 'Golden Period' at the moment. Function is the only real consideration of note at this time as Ellie does not yet have the self-awareness to feel in any way self-conscious about her hand. We – and most of the people who see her regularly – do not even notice her hand any more because she enjoys such good function and doesn't see it as an issue herself.

This will change. We don't want it to. We'd prefer her – and us - to stay in this nice little bubble of innocent ignorance forever but, alas, that's not how life works.

I'd like to think her stubbornness and independent-mindedness will help her to deal with the comments and teasing that will inevitably come her way when she gets a little older. I will of course do all I can to equip her with suitable defence mechanisms and seek to instil in her a degree of confidence that will embolden her to stand up for herself. She has already learnt to stand her ground physically as she fights with Finley all the time now that he's no longer big enough to impose his will on her without retort. It goes without saying that her mother and I will always, always be there to help pick her up whenever she feels down and to give her a kiss and a cuddle whether she wants one or not. She will feel loved – and know that she is loved - every single minute of every single day; there's no doubt about that.

The fact that Ellie's hand function is so good has made us decide not to pursue any of the significant surgical options available that may change its appearance. After several more visits to Addenbrookes and one jaunt to the Great Ormond Street Children's Hospital, we came to the conclusion that transferring one or more toes - the most common surgical action afforded to children born without fingers – had more cons than pros in Ellie's case. Our reasoning here is that we believe having toes on her hand might make her feel even more self conscious when she gets older. We also think that agreeing to a procedure that would leave her with unusual feet as well as a different-looking hand would add to any insecurities she may develop.

This decision was not an easy one to reach. Indeed there were times when we thought completely the opposite. However, it is the one we're sticking to at the moment. The fact that this kind of surgery can be done later on in life gives us a bit of leeway though, so we know we can always do an about-turn if we change our minds.

Whilst it is of course natural to be concerned about Ellie's hand and the potential issues which are likely to arise from it in the future, I have to say that I probably only spend about one per cent of my waking day thinking about such things. The fact is, I very rarely look at Ellie and see anything other than a bright, happy and completely irrepressible little girl. I don't see a 'disadvantaged' child at all; I just see an unbelievably cute and periodically mischievous two-year-old who loves watching *Peppa Pig*, playing hide and seek, and jumping up and down to *Nirvana* songs. It really doesn't matter if her hand isn't like most other peoples. It wouldn't matter to me if she had no hands, no legs, or no ability to speak, listen or see. She is my daughter and I am her Daddy. We both know that – along with her mother - we are the most important people in the world to each other. It is unconditional love and it is the biggest Top Trump you can ever hope to play. Nothing is as fulfilling, as rewarding or as all-encompassing as the love a parent has for a son or daughter and as such no problem, issue, concern or worry is formidable enough to dent the bond that exists between us.

I think of this often when I see my own Mum and Dad playing with Ellie. They moved to the local area a few months after she was born and now come over and babysit two afternoons a week while I work in the bedroom. When the weather's fine the three of them decamp to the garden where I can see and hear them playing through the window. Watching my Mum struggle to get out of a kiddies' teepee whilst Ellie screams "again Granddad, again" at my dad as he pushes her around on her trike gives me a degree of satisfaction and contentment that I never, ever expected to feel.

But I suppose I should have learnt by now: expecting the unexpected is something that comes with the territory when you become a parent...

Acknowledgements

There are a number of people I must thank for supporting me along this journey.

First off are Sal's completely selfless mum and persistently under-appreciated stepdad. You've both made me feel like part of the family from the very first moment I met you and I am eternally grateful for the emotional – and logistical – assistance you've afforded me over the years.

And then there is my own Mum and Dad. I know I'm not an easy person to deal with at times but you always manage see past all my bullshit and give me nothing but love and honesty in return. If I can be half the parent that you have both been to me then I will know I'm on the right lines. Much love always.

Sally. The impact you've had on my life is immeasurable. I adore you and admire you in equal measure as you are the kindest, most genuine person I have ever met. You are, quite simply, the best person I know.

And to Ellie. You have only been with me a relatively short time but you are already my world. You make every day wonderful; I truly cannot conceive of living a life without you. I am so, so proud to call myself your Daddy.

Nods of appreciation must also go out to Clare & John, Ryan, Leanne, Tina & Chris, Tracy & Trevor, and Ricky; good people who have all gone out of their way for our fledgling family at some point or another. You're the best.

53915601R00104

Made in the USA
Charleston, SC
19 March 2016